Residents' Money

A guide to
good practice
in care homes

C000039184

Compiled by Ginny Jenkins

BOOKS

© 1996 Age Concern England
Published by Age Concern England
1268 London Road
London SW16 4ER

Editor Caroline Hartnell
Design and production Eugenie Dodd Typographics
Printed and bound in Great Britain by Bell & Bain Ltd, Glasgow

A catalogue record for this book is available from the British Library.

ISBN 0–86242–205–1

Contents

Foreword

Residents' Money: A guide to good practice in care homes aims to help people who live in care homes to enjoy the fullest use of their own income. The project was funded by the Department of Health and Anchor Housing Trust and ably coordinated by Ginny Jenkins, who is now the director of Action on Elder Abuse. Age Concern is grateful to the many organisations from the statutory, voluntary and private sector who have ensured that the book is suitable not just for homes for elderly people but for those homes whose residents have a learning handicap or physical disability or are mentally ill.

Our aim has been to promote management systems which will give security to staff in promoting the ability of residents to spend their money. I hope that it will prove useful to individuals, staff and relatives of those in care homes.

Sally Greengross
Director General, Age Concern England

Acknowledgements

Managing your own money is hard enough but managing other people's money is fraught with difficulties.

The individual who lives in the care home has to have the same opportunity as any other person to use his or her own money and make choices about its use. At the same time the home must have systems in place to ensure that the money is safe. Guidance on how the balance between these two needs can be achieved has been missing.

In researching this book I heard of many practices which it was insisted are still current:

- people being actively discouraged from keeping any personal money;
- people having to surrender benefit books on entering a home and having no money for a long time;
- people queuing for a weekly cash handout from a communal bowl;
- staff being required to go to the local post office and return with several hundred pounds of benefit payments in cash;
- staff being falsely accused of theft.

The continued occurrence of such practices as these highlights the need for guidance in this area. I would like to thank Age Concern England, and especially Evelyn McEwen, for recognising the need for guidance and giving me the opportunity to write this book. I would also like to thank all those who helped by coming to meetings and commenting on draft manuscripts (see Appendix J for a list of organisations consulted). Their support, patience and enthusiasm encouraged me to finish it.

My especial thanks are due to Dorothy White of the Relatives Association, Heather Wing of the National Association of Inspection and Registration Officers, Pat Rhamdanie of the Royal College of Nursing, Society of Inspection and Registration Officers, and Ann Snell of Age Concern Berkshire. I would also like to thank Des Scully of the Mersey Regional Health Authority, whose publication *A Precious Resource* inspired this work.

Ginny Jenkins

1 | Introduction

People who live in a residential or nursing home or one which is dual-registered have the same right as everyone else to spend, save or give away their own money (weekly income after the home's fees have been paid). Individuals should be able to buy something solely for themselves, or collectively with others, according to their own preference. The role of home management and care workers is to ensure that each person in the home is able, or enabled, to do this.

Some two people in five who live in a home pay their own fees. The fees of the remainder are paid through Income Support or by the local authority with a contribution from the individual. Fees are sometimes paid by a health authority and in certain circumstances there is housing association funding. After the fees have been paid, most people are left with only a modest weekly income. Many rely entirely on the personal expenses allowance. Some will have substantially more money because they receive such benefits as Disability Living Allowance (mobility component) or have income from investments or pensions left after they have paid the fees.

This guide, which covers those living in England and Wales, has been written to set out the basic principles involved in helping individuals to gain maximum benefit from their weekly income. Although the principles apply to those living in Scotland or Northern Ireland, the regulatory system for homes and the legal protection for those who lack capacity are different.

This book makes two important initial assumptions.

First, it assumes that nearly everyone has the ability to be involved in some aspect, however small, of their own financial affairs. However, it recognises that for a few this involvement will be extremely limited and that for even fewer who totally lack capacity this involvement will be through another person who acts as their advocate.

See Appendices F and G.

Second, it assumes that the principles relating to the management of someone's finances, as stated in *Home Life* (see Appendix D), are valid for nursing, residential and dual-registered homes. These include the principle that a home does not have to have any responsibility for or involvement in an individual's financial affairs; where this does occur, however, good practice by the home management will ensure that information is available on ways in which individuals can use their money and how that money can be managed on their behalf. Any system which does not involve the home management should also be based on these principles.

1.1 Who are the 'individuals'?

The individuals referred to in this book are people living in accommodation for older people and for those with a physical disability, with mental health problems or with learning disabilities. Many individuals need guidance and assistance to enable them to benefit from their own money, and the amount of help needed will vary with each person. Some people may, legally, be capable of managing their own financial affairs but need physical assistance, encouragement or support in decision-making.

There will be others who may be legally incapable of managing, so that someone else has to take financial decisions on their behalf. Many people will have relatives, friends or others as their appointees to deal with benefits paid by the Benefits Agency. Some will have an attorney empowered by an enduring power of attorney to be their financial representative, while others will be 'patients' (the Court's term) of the Court of Protection, with another person as the receiver appointed by the court. Only someone who has obtained one of these legal authorities is entitled to manage money on another's behalf.

See section 7.2.

1.2 Who is this book written for?

This book is written for those involved in assisting individuals in residential and nursing home care to manage money. It is aimed, principally, at home managers but could also be a benchmark for anyone else involved in financial management. It should help them to understand the practical issues involved in designing and putting into practice policies to help people to manage their own money. It is hoped that readers will be able to apply the principles stated here within their own sphere of influence.

In practice, this book could be used in a wide range of contexts – in private and voluntary sector residential and nursing homes as well as in residential homes run by local authorities. It could be used by home proprietors or managers to develop practical philosophies and policies, by care workers, and by relatives, voluntary organisations and others who wish to ensure that people who live in homes benefit from their own money. Service purchasers or providers could use it to develop and monitor criteria for service provision. For any of these to be successful, readers need to be aware of the home's procedures for managing an individual's money.

2 | Principles involved

To handle our own money and be involved in transactions connected with it is so much second nature to most of us that we rarely think about its importance. It gives us not only purchasing power but the independence to choose how we use our money.

People who live in a home have similar expectations to people living in the community. They expect to be able to control every aspect of their personal finances in privacy. However, the expectations of many have to be tempered when they realise how little money is left when they have paid the home's fees. Some people, depending on their disability, may need assistance to help them plan, or spend, their money, while others may need someone else to act on their behalf.

Staff and others often assume that, simply because they live in a home, people are incapable of handling some, or all, of their own finances. Both the guidance produced to supplement the Nursing Homes Act 1975 (see Appendix B) and that consolidated in the Registered Homes Act 1984 (see Appendices C and D) clearly state that it must be assumed that an individual has the ability to make financial arrangements, and not the reverse. However, it must be remembered that some people who could manage their own finances will make the positive choice not to do so.

Many people who live in a home may need some help to manage their money. Some may not have relatives or friends who can be involved, or they may not wish to involve them. Others may not know someone who lives near enough to help with the practical, day-to-day issues.

2.1 *Home Life* recommendations

It is therefore increasingly necessary that homes should consider how, taking into account the recommendations of Home Life (see Appendix D), they will make it possible for people who are living there to manage their own money. Any system must not only benefit the individual but be a practical proposition for the home as well. The system should allow the individual financial privacy by ensuring that the direct care worker is not involved unnecessarily in any aspect of that individual's financial affairs. However, since there may be specific circumstances, such as when an individual is learning about money management, when the direct care worker does become involved, the home must make sure that this does not happen except as part of an individual's agreed care plan. Controls and safeguards must be put in place to ensure that an individual's money is secure, but these should never be solely for the convenience of the home or local authority.

At a time when there is pressure on home proprietors to minimise their costs, two facts must be recognised: that good practice costs money and that fundamental to the whole exercise is the recognition that everyone involved may need to change their attitudes.

In order to facilitate this, opportunities for wide-ranging discussions at local level between home proprietors and all others involved are necessary. Individual homes, groups of homes or associations representing homes or any of the other groups involved should take the lead and organise such meetings. Care workers, individuals who live in homes or their representatives, relatives, voluntary sector workers, the regulators, community care managers and other local authority staff should be involved, while representatives of the Benefits Agency, police and other appropriate organisations may also have to be drawn in.

The purpose of these discussions should be to work out ways to ensure that the interests of the individual are paramount, while those of staff and others are not ignored.

13

Ways of facilitating expenditure and ensuring that staff spend time so that individuals benefit should also be examined, as should the cost implications of good practice and how these can be met. Homes should never be expected to absorb all the costs involved themselves.

2.2 Four basic principles

Any guidance relating to the money of people who live in a home must stress four basic principles – all too often ignored by those involved in residential and nursing home care:

- Everyone has the right to have some money to spend.

- Having no money, or always having to ask for it, is a form of restraint and is unacceptable. It is also humiliating.

- An individual's right to conduct his or her financial affairs in private is fundamental.

- It must be assumed that people are capable of managing their financial affairs, rather than the reverse.

3 | Rights and responsibilities

Implicit in having the right to do something is the acknowledgement of the accompanying responsibilities. The main text of this book describes in some detail the rights of the individual and the responsibilities of others to ensure that these rights can be met. It is important that the obverse is also stated and kept in mind: the responsibilities of the person living in the home and the rights of all others involved.

3.1 The individual

When individuals move into a home they need to understand the financial implications and how they will manage their money after admission. How such an understanding is achieved may be a responsibility shared between the individual and the home, although others, such as relatives and advocates, may share that responsibility. The local authority financial assessor responsible under the NHS and Community Care Act may need to be involved in assisting understanding prior to admission.

It may involve understanding the answers to a series of questions but, whatever the method used, the result should be that the individual clearly understands such issues as security of tenure, the services to which the contract costs relate, and the circumstances under which additional costs may be incurred.

When living in the home individuals should not keep more cash or valuables there than are covered by either the home's or their own insurance. If they do so, they must take full responsibility for any losses which result.

If the home is looking after their money, individuals should be considerate and not be unreasonable in their requests to the home management for cash or information.

Individuals should plan for the future in case at some time they no longer wish to, or are no longer able to, manage money. It may be prudent to prepare an enduring power of attorney.

3.2 The relatives

Relatives should expect to be treated with sensitivity by staff and others as they adjust to the implications of someone living in a home. If the individual has a mental, physical or learning disability the relative may have to adjust to no longer living with someone for whom they have cared for years. Where the individual is an older person, relatives may have to adjust to managing, and even supplementing, the dwindling resources of someone who was, previously, financially independent.

Relatives are often in a difficult position. They may feel that they have the right, and indeed the responsibility, to raise, and if necessary pursue, any concerns they may have about the way in which an individual's money is being managed and spent. However, they must also respect that person's right to privacy and confidentiality and above all to spend the money as he or she chooses.

3.3 The home proprietor

Because a home is a business, it is essential that it has a positive cash flow. The purchaser of care or the individual should ensure that management is always paid promptly, efficiently and in full for the services provided.

Home staff and management should follow the recommendations of *Home Life* (see Appendix D) and *Registration and inspection of nursing homes – A handbook for health authorities* (see Appendix B). While this means that an individual's money should be appropriately managed, the home does not have to be directly involved.

3.4 The regulators

3.4.1 Nursing homes

Nursing home inspectors should investigate complaints about a home's management of an individual's money. They are also recommended to investigate any concerns raised about a home's management of a person's financial affairs but they have no statutory right to do so.

See Appendix B.

3.4.2 Residential homes

Where a residential home manages an individual's financial affairs, the inspector from the Registration and Inspection Unit has the right to inspect all the home's records relating to that management to ensure that the person's finances are being properly dealt with.

The Registration and Inspection Unit has the right to be informed by the Department of Social Security if a home manager is made an appointee for anyone who lives in the home.

It has the right to investigate any complaints made about financial management.

These rights also apply to homes which are managed by a local authority.

See Appendices C and D.

4 | Sources of income

4.1 Personal income

People's income may be made up from some or all of the following sources:

- personal, occupational and war pensions;
- trusts, investments, property, savings and other personal income;
- the State Basic Pension and State Earnings-Related Pension (SERPS), Income Support, Incapacity Benefit, Severe Disablement Allowance, Disability Living Allowance, Attendance Allowance or Industrial Injury Benefits.

4.1.1 Disability Living Allowance and Attendance Allowance

The care component of Disability Living Allowance (DLA Care) and Attendance Allowance (AA) are payable only for the first four weeks of someone's stay in a home if they are being funded by the local authority.

If the place is temporary, any DLA Care and AA paid during the first four weeks is not counted as income by the local authority.

DLA Care and AA continue to be paid to those who enter a home and pay the full fees themselves, except for those who live in a local authority home. For this group, DLA Care and AA cease after four weeks and they have to pay the difference themselves. People planning to go into a local authority home who will be paying their own fees should be made aware of this.

The mobility component of Disability Living Allowance (DLA Mobility) is payable to anyone who qualifies regardless of where they live. It is not regarded as income for the financial assessment by the local authority under the NHS and Community Care Act 1990. It is available to people who become disabled before they are 65 but they must be under 66 years of age when they apply for it.

DLA Care, DLA Mobility and AA are benefits which are often not claimed. Even if DLA Care and AA cannot be paid because an individual receives local authority funding, it is still important that they are claimed and any underlying entitlement established as there may be times when they can be paid. These would include when an individual has temporarily left the home to stay with relatives for a holiday or if the individual's financial status changes.

4.1.2 Income Support

Income Support is not available to anyone in a home who has savings of more than £8,000. This will rise to £16,000 by April 1996. It includes severe disability premium (SDP) for those who receive AA or DLA Care (middle or highest level). The SDP usually continues for as long as DLA Care/AA is paid. This is normally four weeks where the local authority has made the arrangement. Where people have made their own arrangements in a private or voluntary home, it may continue as long as they pay their own fees.

4.2 Personal expenses allowance

From April 1993, anyone who enters a home and is financially supported by the local authority must be allowed to retain part of their income as a personal expenses allowance (PEA). Its level is set by Parliament each year, and the allowance cannot be used by the local authority to contribute to the home's basic fee.

People who went to live in a home before April 1993 may be having their fees paid under 'preserved rights' to Income Support. For this group of people, the personal expenses allowance may be used, if they wish, to pay part of the home's basic fee if the fee is more than the Income Support ceiling.

4.3 Information on benefits

The State benefit system is complex and subject to changes. It is therefore not unusual for benefits not to have been claimed and sometimes substantial arrears payments may be due. It is essential to check that people receive their full entitlement to benefit, and in particular whether they are entitled to AA/DLA Care and SDP after entering a home.

Individuals may need assistance with any benefits check. In certain situations a relative or care staff at the home may feel able to assume this role. In addition to the Benefits Agency, further assistance from the following local resources may be available:

■ welfare rights services;

■ social workers;

■ Citizens Advice Bureaux;

■ local MIND, MENCAP, Age Concern organisations.

At national level, assistance may be sought from the Disability Alliance, Age Concern England, MIND or MENCAP.

4.3.1 The Benefits Agency

Local Benefits Agency officers may hold detailed discussions with individuals about their claims. The officer may be able to visit the home where the individual is living if required.

The address and telephone number of the local agency can be found listed under 'Benefits Agency' in the telephone directory.

The free Disability Benefits Enquiry Line will give advice and information about disability benefits. Tel: 0800 88 22 00.

A free form completion service is available on 0800 44 11 44.

4.3.2 How State benefits are paid

One or more benefit books may be issued for any benefits and pensions payable. These can be cashed weekly at the local post office or sub-post office. Alternatively, benefits can be paid by girocheque, 'payable order cheque', or direct into a bank or building society account. When benefits are paid into a bank account, Income Support is paid weekly, while other benefits are paid fortnightly, four-weekly or quarterly in arrears.

As a security measure and to improve customer service, benefit order books and girocheques are being phased out. They will be replaced gradually by benefit payment cards over the period 1996–99.

If people have a bank or building society account, payment directly into the account through Automated Credit Transfer (ACT) may enable them to receive their money more easily when they can no longer go to the post office. However, no one should be pressured into opening an account or being paid by ACT against their wishes.

4.3.3 Agent and appointee

People who cannot go to a post office or sub-post office to cash benefits may appoint an agent to do so on their behalf. The role of the agent is strictly limited to cashing the benefit. It is an informal arrangement and the agent has no legal power to direct how the money is spent.

However, if individuals cannot manage their finances, because of mental disorder or incapacity, a person holding an enduring power of attorney, a receiver or someone else can become an appointee to receive and spend State benefits on their behalf.

Applications to act as appointee for benefit purposes are made to the Benefits Agency. An appointee takes on full personal responsibility for the correct claiming of benefits, as if they were the beneficiary themselves. This includes reporting any changes which may affect benefit entitlement (eg capital assets, state of incapacity, etc). It is therefore important that an appointee is someone who is fully aware of the individual's circumstances. An appointee may direct how the money is spent and may be required to repay any benefit which has been overpaid.

See section 7.2 and Appendices F and G.

5 | Paying home fees

People who entered a home on or after 1 April 1993 will either be paying their own fees or having their fees paid in whole or in part by a local authority under the NHS and Community Care Act. Many people are currently paying their own fees. In either case, the way in which fees are paid, the additional charges which may be incurred, and what may or may not be done with residual income is very important.

People who entered a home before 1 April 1993 may be having their home fees paid under 'preserved rights' to Income Support. This usually continues if they move to a new home, although the rate payable will be based on that fixed as appropriate for the category into which the new home falls. If there is a shortfall between the home's charge and the maximum amount payable by the Department of Social Security (DSS), this will have to be met from some other source, usually relatives or charitable donations. The local authority has some very limited powers to help in this situation.

5.1 Safeguards

Where the local authority pays all or part of the home's fee, systems of financial management should be stated in the local authority contract with the home. Since no standard national contract exists, requirements vary from authority to authority.

The Association of Metropolitan Authorities, the Association of County Councils and the Association of

Directors of Social Services have prepared written guidance on a model contract which they hope will be adopted as standard for an 'out-of-authority' contract, ie a contract with a home not geographically situated within the authority's boundary. This should reduce the number of systems a home has to run to a maximum of two. It is hoped that all homes will operate to the same high standard for people living there who pay their own fees.

Safeguards to protect the management of an individual's finances can be included as a condition of any local authority contract. The 40 per cent who make their own contract with a home have no protection, other than that contained in their contract with the home.

Everyone who lives in a registered residential home is protected by the Registered Homes Act 1984, its regulations and the tribunal findings which have reinforced the code of practice *Home Life*. People in nursing homes also have rights under the same Act and the accompanying National Association of Health Authorities and Trusts (NAHAT) guidance, but these are not necessarily the same.

5.2 Pre-admission information

When choosing a home, it is important to be able to compare accurately what each home's stated price includes. Only when this full information is available can individuals choose how to spend their money.

These details should be clearly laid out in the information given to everyone considering living in a home and given to them again when they take up residence. Pre-admission information should include:

- what is and what is not included in the basic fee;
- the charges for any additional items;
- the fee review date;
- guidelines for possible increases in fees, eg in line with any increase in DSS rates;
- how to get information on DSS benefits, especially those which alter as a result of living in a home;

- details of the ways in which individuals are enabled to manage their own money and how it might be managed if they do not wish to, or cannot, manage it themselves;
- notice requirements and any fee payable after an individual has died;
- level of fee payable if the room is sub-let during an individual's absence;
- how to make a complaint.

See Appendices B, C and D.

Helpful leaflets
Specific information leaflets are produced by some local authorities, banks and building societies.

5.3 State benefits
These benefits are paid to the individual directly or through an agent, appointee or receiver (see section 7.2). The individual or their representative then has the responsibility to pay the fee due. Arrangements can be made under specific circumstances for the Benefits Agency to pay the home direct.

5.3.1 Payment under the National Assistance Act
The local authority can pay the home the full fee, and collect from the individual their assessed contribution (see below). Any State benefits except DLA Mobility will be counted as income when the individual's contribution is assessed.

If the individual, the home and the local authority all agree, both the local authority and the individual can pay their share of the fee direct to the home.

5.3.1.1 *Contributions due to the local authority* Individuals whose fees are paid following a financial assessment by the local authority will have to pay an assessed contribution to the authority. The level of contribution is decided by statutory means test. The assessed contribution may be paid either to the local authority or, by agreement with the authority, direct to the home.

Individuals are expected to claim all social security benefits available to them and should be helped to do this. These are normally paid to individuals who then pay their assessed personal contribution either to the local authority or direct to the home, depending on what arrangements have been made. State benefits may also be paid directly to the local authority, if the authority has been made the appointee or where, under specific circumstances, direct payments have been agreed.

5.3.1.2 **Financial assessment** The financial assessment for an individual's contribution to the cost of residential or nursing home care under the NHS and Community Care Act is separate from the needs assessment. It should take place after the needs assessment has indicated that living in a residential or nursing home is the best solution.

The assessment consists of two parts: the declaration of an individual's assets and its analysis. The declaration is often undertaken by the care manager. The analysis is carried out by a finance officer of the local authority and the results may not be known for some time.

The financial assessment follows national rules but local authorities have some discretion in certain circumstances (see LAC(95)7 *Charges for Residential Accommodation – Amendment no. 5*, which is a complete update of the *Charging for Residential Accommodation Guide (CRAG)*).

Where individuals are admitted to a home in an emergency or where it has been impossible to complete the analysis before admission, they should be told how they will be kept informed of its progress and results. Once the local authority has completed the assessment, it must tell the individual of the results immediately.

While the assessment is being completed, a local authority should not take an individual's benefit book without obtaining his/her permission; and, if the person has no other source of income, the authority must ensure that the individual has some money to spend.

Because of the way benefits interact with home charges, there is usually at least one change in the charge in the first four weeks. It is important that the accuracy of the assessment is checked carefully.

Helpful leaflets

Age Concern England Factsheet 10 *Local authority charging procedures for residential and nursing home care.*

5.4 Third-party payments – topping up

If the local authority agrees to provide, or arrange the provision of, a place in a care home, a relative or someone else may 'top up' this to pay for more expensive facilities than are required to meet the person's assessed needs if the individual so wishes. Additional payments made in this way are not regarded as part of the individual's income for benefit purposes.

The right to make additional payments is clearly stated in Circular LAC(92)27 *The National Assistance 1948 (Choice of Accommodation) Directions (1992)* and Circular LAC (93)18 *The National Assistance Act 1948 (Choice of Accommodation) (Amendment) Directions (1993).*

Following good practice, local authorities and home proprietors will inform relatives or others, including charitable donors, who are making third-party payments about what will happen if their personal circumstances change. Those making such payments should be aware that, if they stop, the individual may no longer be able to stay in the home and alternative, cheaper accommodation may have to be found.

5.5 Block contract

Local authorities may purchase 'blocks of accommodation', ie undertake to buy a number of places in a home from providers, which may mean that they can buy care cost-effectively. However, individuals still have the right to choose the accommodation they wish within the constraints on choice stated in Circular LAC(92)27 and LAC(93)18. After taking these limitations into account, an individual still has the right to choose, and this should not be affected by local authority purchases.

5.6 Local authority-purchased accommodation outside its own boundaries

Circular LAC(92)27 enables a local authority to purchase accommodation within another authority, if it will benefit the individual, for example by enabling them to live near a relative.

6 | Choice

People must be able to do as *they* choose with *their* money

Individuals should be able to choose how to spend, save or give away their own money.

Having paid the home's fee or their assessed contribution, they may choose to spend their money on anything else they wish, whether it is non-durable items, such as soap, fruit or magazines, or more durable items, such as clothes, pictures or furniture. Purchases may be made daily, once a week or once a year, for example on a holiday, or even once in a lifetime, such as for a granddaughter's wedding.

Some people may feel that those who live in homes spend, or risk spending, money inappropriately, and that they should be protected by, for instance, being made 'patients' of the Court of Protection.

The crucial difference between what others see as foolish expenditure and the lack of capacity to make decisions about money must be recognised. While mismanagement of personal finances may indicate incapacity, formal procedures must never be implemented just because someone makes unwise judgements or because appropriate systems are not in place to help individuals make the best use of their money.

In some cases it may be wise for individuals to prepare a financial programme setting out priorities and balancing various calls on income, with assistance from others if necessary.

See Appendix F.

6.1 Helping people to choose

The individual may want help and support from family and/or care workers in choosing how to spend money. An independent advocate – someone who has absolutely no vested interest in what the person decides – should be available to support them and communicate their views on how their money should be spent. Individuals should always have access to an advocate if they want advice. It may be appropriate for a relative or a care worker to undertake the role of advocate. However, it must not be assumed that this is always what an individual wants.

Further assistance may be available from local MIND, MENCAP or Age Concern organisations.

See Appendices C and D.

6.2 Limitations on expenditure

The first call on an individual's income must be the home's fee or that person's assessed contribution to it under the financial assessment.

6.2.1 Debts

No general rule makes anyone else responsible for another's debts, although spouses may have a common law responsibility for each other's debts. The contract with the home may specify that a spouse or other relative is responsible for the individual's debts. Under such circumstances the relative concerned must be aware that the home cannot oblige them to accept this responsibility, and if they do decide to agree they must think through the possible implications for the future.

Where a local authority has purchased the place, the individual must not be invoiced or have the personal expenses allowance reduced by a home because the authority owes the home money.

6.2.2 Savings

Individuals may choose:

■ to save all, part or none of their income;

■ to save with no specific end in view;

- to save with a major expense in mind, such as a holiday;
- to save to enable their money to last as long as possible.

Some people are savers, some are spenders; some will feel secure only if they have a nest egg. People in residential or nursing homes usually have diminishing incomes, so their opportunities to amass savings are limited.

Many individuals, especially older people, feel that it is important that an individual has 'enough money to bury them' and are distressed by the idea of a 'pauper's' funeral. Others may lay equal importance on being able to leave something, however small, to their friends, family or children.

Some people, however, especially those who realised capital assets before admission or who have savings which accrued while they were living in long-stay hospitals, may have savings of many thousands of pounds. Individuals who live in a home should be aware that savings over £3,000 will decrease the amount of Income Support they receive, and that if their savings exceed £8,000 Income Support will not be payable. However, by April 1996 these figures will change to £10,000 and £16,000.

The same savings rules apply to financial assistance received from local authorities as these are, for the most part, in line with the Income Support rules.

See section 8.4.7

6.2.3 Dry cleaning and laundry

If individuals choose to have clothes dry-cleaned or hand-washed they must expect to pay the costs involved. The laundering of machine-washable clothing should be included in the home's basic charge.

6.2.4 Gratuities and tips

The soliciting of gratuities by staff is always unacceptable and should always be in contravention of the contract of employment.

Whether staff should be allowed to receive cash gratuities or tips is always a difficult issue. While individuals may wish to offer or give gratuities to care workers or other staff, this is best discouraged.

The home should have a clear policy on this subject which is known to residents, their visitors and the staff. The policy should be consistent with that on gifts and legacies. It must state if staff accepting gratuities are contravening their contract of employment. If it is a contravention of their contract of employment for staff to accept gratuities, this must be stated.

Where a home's policy is that staff may accept gratuities, these must always be reported to the home management.

See section 8.5.

6.2.5 Gifts

Individuals may, if they wish, give gifts in cash or in kind to any other person or group of people, whether they are staff, relatives, friends they live with or friends living elsewhere.

Gifts of cards, calendars or ornaments of minimal value made by individuals themselves can avoid the inherent dangers of giving cash or expensive, purchased gifts to staff, and may mean more to both the giver and the receiver.

Care must be taken that individuals are not coerced into giving presents to care workers or people they live with.

Home proprietors should have a known policy on staff receiving gifts. This must be consistent with the policy on gratuities and tips, and the proprietor should ensure that people who live in the home, their visitors and the staff are aware of it.

Procedures should allow for care workers to receive presents but should incorporate the safeguard that all gifts must be recorded and that the home proprietor should be informed when even token presents are received.

See Appendix D.

6.2.6 Holidays

Holidays are regarded as an important feature in many people's lives.

No geographical limitation should be placed on where an individual's holiday takes place.

Individuals should be involved in choosing where they want to go and in planning their holidays, and they should be informed at an early stage of the expected cost and its implication for their annual income.

An individual may be asked to contribute in part or in full to the cost of a holiday.

Holidays taken by those on very low incomes may have to be modest and it may be necessary to seek additional sources of finance, for example by applying to the home's League of Friends or to grant-giving voluntary organisations.

The individual whose fees are paid under 'preserved rights' or the National Assistance Act must expect to pay their assessed contribution to the fees while on holiday. Where individuals pay their own fees, they must pay the cost specified in the contract during any absence. If the contract allows for the room to be sub-let when the individual is absent, he or she should not be charged for it.

The home should have a clear policy for all holidays except those organised by individuals themselves. The policy should state that where the holiday is organised for everyone living in the home, any charge should be agreed by all residents. There should be no charge unless all residents agree otherwise. However, individuals who have the ability to pay should be allowed to make a donation towards the cost if they wish.

The policy should include the statement that where the home encourages fundraising activities to subsidise the cost of a holiday these should be undertaken by a League of Friends or other similar organisation. Such money as is raised for events must be held in a separate account from that of the home. While the home should not be involved in any such fundraising activities, it may allow free use of its facilities.

6.2.7 Outings

An individual can choose to pay for the care worker's incidental expenses during an outing but only if this is an active choice and not out of coercion. Where meals and entrance fees are involved, an individual can pay these as long as they are an integral part of the outing. Individuals should not be expected to pay for, or contribute to, better meals or drinks for care workers than they themselves are having, nor should they be expected to pay for staff expenses on every occasion.

The home proprietor should have a clear policy on charging individuals for outings. Unless the policy and the contract with the individual clearly say so, an individual should not be asked to contribute to the cost of an outing.

Where the home encourages fundraising activities to subsidise the cost of outings, these should be undertaken by a League of Friends or other similar organisation. Money raised in this way must be held in a separate account from that of the home. While the home should not be involved in any such fundraising activities, it may allow free use of its facilities.

A simple, clear system for recording the expenses of an outing and who has paid them should be in place.

6.2.8 Joint purchases

Some or all of a group of people who live together may combine to buy something which they cannot afford individually. These joint purchases are usually for large items such as garden furniture or a music centre.

The principles to be followed are:

■ In the final analysis, the individual's wishes are the most important.

■ Decisions on joint purchases must be taken by the individuals concerned. Where appropriate, a relative, advocate, attorney, appointee or receiver, and the home proprietor, should also be consulted before the purchase is made.

- All the people making the purchase must be able to benefit from it.

- Each person's financial contribution should reflect the total amount they have available to spend and their anticipated use. It must be possible for each person to have his or her contribution reimbursed, after allowing for an item's depreciation or appreciation, should he or she change their mind or leave the home. It must be possible for an individual's estate to benefit from the money on that person's death.

A home should have clear guidance on joint purchases. It must include information on the level of agreement required for such purchases, as well as on how contributions are to be repaid.

6.2.9 Visitors' expenses

Individuals may choose to pay their visitors' expenses. These may be the cost of travelling to the home, drinks, a meal or an overnight stay.

The charges, and circumstances under which a home makes charges for visitors' accommodation or refreshments, should be clearly stated.

6.2.10 Equipment for disability

6.2.10.1 *Nursing homes* The nursing home should be equipped with a range of daily living and nursing equipment, including equipment to promote continence.

See Appendix E, sections 25.2, 25.4.6, 25.4.10, 25.4.12.

6.2.10.1.1 *Daily living equipment* The level of standard provision will have been established with the regulator as part of the registration process.

Where individuals require different equipment, the home should help them to obtain it either on loan from the local authority or by enabling them to buy it if they wish.

6.2.10.1.2 **Nursing equipment** In general, a home is expected to provide the level of equipment required by an individual on admission and it should not admit people for whom it does not have appropriate equipment. Nor should it be approached to admit someone who needs very specialist equipment and be expected to purchase these items if they are unlikely to be of more general use. In such cases an agreement as to who will provide them will have to be reached between the purchaser (whether an authority or an individual) and the home.

Under certain circumstances an individual may wish to pay for nursing equipment which is to a higher specification than that which is provided as standard.

See Appendix E, sections 25.4.3–25.4.3.2.1.

6.2.10.2 **Residential homes**

6.2.10.2.1 **Daily living equipment** Individuals should not be expected to pay for equipment which can be loaned from a local authority, though they may choose to buy it instead.

A residential home is expected, as a condition of registration, to provide a specified level of daily living equipment.

If one person needs specific equipment, he or she is entitled to be assessed for provision by the local social services department. The equipment should be loaned on the same basis as for any other person who lives in the community, although in practice those who live in a residential home may be given lower priority.

The residential home is expected to make it possible for someone's specific requirements to be met by arranging an assessment by the local social services department.

See Appendix E.

6.2.10.2.2 **Nursing equipment** People who live in a residential home should have the same access to community nursing care through a district nurse as those who live in the community. They should also receive on loan any necessary nursing equipment from a health authority. In practice, however, as with daily living equipment, these individuals may be given lower priority. Similarly, individuals may choose to buy items for themselves.

The residential home is expected to help the needs of a specific person to be met by arranging an assessment by the local district nursing service.

See Appendix E, section 24.4.3

6.2.11 Therapy services and equipment

6.2.11.1 *Nursing homes* If required, therapy services should be provided by the nursing home. It should also be clear whether this is provided by the National Health Service or a private practitioner. The level of provision of physiotherapy, occupational therapy, speech therapy and chiropody included in the home's basic fee should be clearly stated.

Individuals who require additional treatment have the right to be referred for NHS treatment which is free at the point of delivery or to pay for private treatment. The cost of additional treatment and the qualifications of the practitioners providing the treatment should be clearly stated.

The home must facilitate this additional treatment and has a responsibility to ensure that people are aware of their entitlement to free treatment.

Therapy equipment, such as walking aids, may be purchased by the individual or loaned by either the local social services department or the health authority.

See Appendix E.

6.2.11.2 *Residential homes* Homes are not required to provide therapy services and equipment as part of their basic service. However, a residential home should make it possible for its residents to have access to physiotherapy, occupational therapy, speech therapy or chiropody, by arranging for either NHS or private treatment. Where the treatment arranged is private the qualifications of the practitioners should be stated.

An individual requiring treatment may choose to be referred for NHS treatment which is free at the point of delivery or to pay for private treatment.

Therapy equipment, such as walking aids, may be purchased by the individual or loaned by either the local social services department or the health services.

See Appendix E, section 24.4.6

6.2.12 Other medical services

Dental treatment, eye tests and glasses are available on the NHS with graduated fees dependent on income or they may be purchased privately. Hearing aids continue to be available free on the NHS for individuals who live in both residential and nursing homes.

Residential and nursing homes should have appropriate specialist equipment, such as induction loops for people with hearing impairment, as routine fixtures.

See Appendix E, sections 24.4.6, 24.4.7.

7 | Control

Individuals must be in control – assume first that they are capable of controlling their own money, not the reverse

No barriers should be put in the way of individuals spending their own money as they wish. Individuals should always be assumed to be capable of managing and controlling their own affairs unless medical or legal processes have formally judged otherwise (see section 7.1).

In residential or nursing home care, too often the reverse is assumed.

People who can manage their own affairs have an absolute right to decide how their money is spent.

They also have the right, if they so wish, to decline to manage their own money and, having clearly stated this, to request that a representative act on their behalf.

It is important to recognise that many people are not competent to manage every aspect of their financial affairs but are capable of managing some aspects. It is therefore very important to understand the difference between capacity, which is the legal term for competence, and the results of making errors of judgement. We all make errors of judgement, some of which have grave consequences, but it does not mean that we lack the capacity to manage our own affairs.

Someone who lives in a home and apparently makes foolish decisions, for instance giving away the entire personal expenses allowance or spending it all on chocolate, may be lacking in capacity, but this must not be assumed. Nor should processes to make individuals 'patients' of the Court of Protection be started simply because they have a small capital balance which others feel should be protected.

Individuals who have been judged to be lacking the capacity to manage their own affairs must still be consulted as far as is possible as to how their money is to be spent.

It must be remembered that some people may in time gain or regain their capacity to manage their financial affairs. Formal protection procedures should then be reversed.

Where a home has any involvement in an individual's financial affairs, it has a duty to ensure that, if an individual's capacity to manage their financial affairs has decreased, State benefits are paid to an appointee rather than an agent, and an attorney appointed under an enduring power of attorney is told of the need to register the power with the Court of Protection. Where appropriate, it should also ensure that relatives are informed of the need to apply to the Court of Protection for the appointment of a receiver.

See section 7.2 and Appendices B, D, F and G.

7.1 **Assessing competence**

When an individual enters a home, their capacity to manage their own money should always be assessed as part of the admission procedure. If following the assessment the home manager feels that there are causes for concern, these should be discussed with the individual, their doctor (in case there is a treatable cause), relatives and the care manager or social worker as suggested below. If there are doubts about someone's capacity it is always advisable to discuss this with the individual's doctor.

If people are already living in a home their capacity to handle their own finances should be reviewed regularly as part of the home's care plan for them. If the home manager feels that capacity has altered, the same course of action as suggested above should be taken. Where an individual no longer has a care manager or social worker, the home should request that one is appointed. The home should be prepared to suggest the appointment of an appointee, the registration of an enduring power of attorney or the instigation of proceedings to appoint a receiver under the Court of Protection.

For people who live in a home following a community care assessment, the care manager should be informed of any change in financial competence as this alters the assessment of need.

People who are self-funding or who have 'preserved rights' should be assessed by the home on admission. If, either at this time or subsequently, the home is concerned about their competence, it should discuss the problem with a relative and/or advocate. Where there is still concern a social worker should also be involved.

See section 8.4.11 and Appendices D, F and G.

7.2 **Types of protection available**

7.2.1 Appointee

If individuals are mentally incapable of handling their own affairs someone (the appointee) can, on application, be appointed by the Benefits Agency, acting on behalf of the Secretary of State for Social Security, to act on that individual's behalf in all social security matters.

Appointees can claim any benefit, receive payments and spend them. They are also responsible for reporting any relevant changes affecting the individual's benefit and refunding any overpaid benefit. Anyone can make an application to be an appointee, but evidence, usually medical, must be available to prove that the individual is incapable of managing his or her affairs. An officer of the Benefits Agency acting on behalf of the Secretary of State must also be satisfied that the person making the application to act as appointee is suitable.

Once appointed, the appointee does not routinely have to account for expenditure to the Benefits Agency or anyone else. If concerns are raised with the Benefits Agency it can query how the money has been spent. The power to act as appointee can be revoked and an alternative person be appointed if the appointee is not acting responsibly.

The appointment is for the purpose of payment of State benefits only. It does not entitle the appointee to undertake any other transactions on the part of the individual or to deal with capital or savings belonging to that individual.

The appointee has an important responsibility to inform the Benefits Agency of changes which may alter benefit levels. These may be the result of increases in an occupational pension or savings.

See section 7.3.

7.2.2 Power of attorney

A power of attorney is a legal document, usually drawn up by a solicitor, which can be shown as proof that another person or persons, possibly a relative or relatives, has been authorised to undertake transactions on an individual's behalf. It gives no legal protection to those who manage money for people who have lost capacity. A power of attorney need not be granted to an appointee (see above).

Power of attorney must be given by people who can understand what they are doing. In the case of an 'ordinary' (not an 'enduring') power of attorney, that power becomes invalid when the individual concerned becomes incapable.

7.2.3 Enduring power of attorney

An enduring power of attorney (EPA), to which additional safeguards are attached, is given by people in case they *become* incapable of managing their financial affairs. An EPA can be drawn up to operate initially as an ordinary power of attorney and, when required, to be registered as an enduring power. As with an ordinary power of attorney, it can be given to more than one person who can then act jointly (together) or either jointly or severally (together or independently), according to what has been specified.

When the attorney believes that the donor is becoming or has become mentally incapable, the attorney has a duty to register the EPA with the Public Trustee. Once the EPA is registered the attorney can act or continue to act for the donor.

The attorney owes the individual a duty of care in carrying out any function under the power and should act in accordance with the intention stated by the individual who gave the power.

It may be appropriate for the individual to prepare an EPA before, or shortly after, admission to a home if this has not been done previously. The form to create an EPA may be purchased from a law stationers or prepared for the donor by a solicitor. Advice should always be sought from a solicitor to ensure that the document is correctly drafted.

7.2.4 Court of Protection

The Court of Protection, an office of the Supreme Court, becomes involved where anyone with an interest, for example a spouse, relative or friend, applies to the Court because it is felt that an individual is no longer capable of managing his or her own affairs and that their financial affairs need to be protected. If an individual has not created an EPA the court can be requested to appoint a receiver for an individual, who is then said to be a 'patient' of the Court.

Even where the Court has assumed jurisdiction over an individual's financial affairs, it may well decide that the individual can carry on managing some aspects of his or her affairs. For example, some 'patients' continue to collect their State benefits and operate bank accounts under the supervision of a receiver. The Court expects receivers to ask it to agree to such an arrangement where it is felt to be appropriate.

7.2.4.1 *Receivership orders* Before receivership orders can be granted, medical evidence must be given that individuals are mentally incapable of managing their own affairs. A person called the receiver is appointed to manage money and assets for the benefit of the 'patient'.

The Court requires accounts to be submitted and must agree to any expenditure above a certain amount. The amount for each patient is set by the Court. The Court must also give prior approval to any transaction which involves capital assets, legal proceedings, or making loans or gifts.

A receivership order is normally only implemented when someone has what the Court considers substantial capital or income (£5,000 in 1995). The Court's annual fee is on a sliding scale assessed on an individual's net income after tax has been paid.

The Court expects the receiver or other authorised person to consult regularly with the individual to try and establish his or her views, as far as is practical, on how the money should be spent. Should the receiver feel unable to agree with an individual's wishes, the receiver should consult the Court, which will decide what course is to be followed. Individuals should also know of their right to raise problems directly with the Court.

7.2.4.2 *Short orders* Where an individual's estate (money, funds and other property) is straightforward and worth less than £5,000, a short order can be made. This contains a few directions authorising someone else to use money or property in certain specified ways to benefit the 'patient'. The Court checks each year that its order is being complied with. The Court can insist that this order is converted to a receivership order if it feels that circumstances warrant it.

Helpful leaflets
Enduring Power of Attorney and *Handbook for Receivers*, available from the Public Trust Office.

7.3 Choosing an appointee or receiver

7.3.1 Spouse, relative or friend

In many cases, a spouse, relative or friend will be the appointee or receiver for someone living in a home. He or she manages the income, liaising with the local authority and home as appropriate. This system makes the home's task easy and ensures that problems such as confidentiality and security are minimised. In the case of receivers, where more than one person are acting jointly, the home may find it helpful to ask them to agree who will have the main responsibility in relation to the home.

However, it must be recognised that:

- Not everyone may want a relative to manage his or her financial affairs.
- Not all relatives spend an individual's income to that person's benefit.
- Relatives and care workers may not agree on the amount of a person's money that should be spent and what it should be spent on.

7.3.2 Financial managers

Traditionally, several different professional groups have offered financial management for those who no longer wish to manage, or are incapable of managing, their own financial affairs. These include solicitors, accountants and bank staff. The amount charged for administering someone's affairs may depend on the number of transactions undertaken on an individual's behalf, but the charges can be high.

A financial manager should have no connection with the home either as part of its management team or employed by it in any capacity.

7.3.3 The Public Trustee

Where an individual has no one else to act as receiver, the Public Trustee may be appointed. People who have the Public Trustee as their receiver pay a higher fee to the Court of Protection than those who do not.

7.3.4 The home proprietor

Although the home proprietor may be prepared to manage an individual's financial affairs, and larger groups of homes may have a specific finance department, it should be remembered that no available guidance recommends this. It should therefore be considered only as a last resort, and all the parties involved must ensure that the appropriate safeguards are observed.

Where the home proprietor is a local authority, it often acts as the appointee or receiver for those living in its homes.

Local authorities should consider the advisability of this and ensure that there is no conflict of interest.

See sections 6.1 and 8.4.2 and Appendix D.

7.3.5 Problems involved

The appointee, attorney or receiver is expected to act in the interests of the individual. Occasionally there are difficulties, and the manager, care worker or someone else feels that an individual is not receiving the full benefit from his or her money.

This problem can be avoided by explaining how the individual can benefit from expenditure, and involving the appointee, attorney or receiver in the planning. Difficulties most commonly occur where home staff are reluctant to talk to the appointee, attorney or receiver, especially where this is a relative. The longer the situation has existed the more difficult it is to tackle as the relatives may have come to regard an individual's money as their own and/or become dependent on this additional source of income.

Action should always be taken as soon as it is felt that an individual is not being given at least the same level of opportunities as the other people with whom they live with similar incomes.

7.3.5.1 *Informal approach* This situation may be difficult to resolve. It will need to be handled with tact and understanding.

The home manager should arrange to meet the appointee, attorney or receiver concerned. At this meeting the manager should explain how it is felt that an individual can benefit further from his or her own money, and try to involve the appointee, attorney or receiver in any plans to spend it. The fears and concerns of the appointee, attorney or receiver should be discussed.

The appointee, attorney or receiver should be reassured that:

- The money will be properly spent and they will be told of the ways in which the individual will benefit.
- They will be told what has been bought and receive receipts.

- They will continue to be involved in decisions about expenditure.

They should be told that if there continues to be concern that an individual is failing to benefit from the money the home will apply to have an alternative appointee or receiver appointed. Alternative attorneys cannot be appointed.

The appointee or receiver should be told how to contact the Citizens Advice Bureau if they need further advice or information. Age Concern, MIND, MENCAP and the Relatives Association will also provide this.

7.3.5.2 *Formal approach* Where a home continues to be concerned about an individual's appointee or receiver, it should approach the individual's advocate or social worker to request that formal approaches be made through the Benefits Agency or the Court of Protection to have the appointee or receiver changed. If the individual has no social worker to act in this situation, the home may request that one is appointed or approach the Court of Protection itself.

Where an enduring power of attorney exists, the Court of Protection must be asked to cancel the power. An alternative attorney cannot be appointed. The individual will then need to become a 'patient' of the Court of Protection.

8 | Management

Management should be efficient but not obstruct an individual's choice

A residential or nursing home which is involved in any aspect of managing an individual's money must have clear procedures for managing and recording it. These should ensure effective control but not create barriers to the individual's freedom to make choices and manage his or her money.

8.1 The local authority's accountability

The purchaser of the care package should be accountable to individuals or their representatives for ensuring that, through its contract, the individual has appropriate management of his or her financial affairs while living in a home.

8.2 The local authority's responsibilities

Through its contract with the residential or nursing home, a purchaser should actively promote flexible and imaginative policies which will enable individuals to benefit from their money. The contract should require that the home has procedures for collecting and banking benefits and other income on behalf of residents and for accounting to the individual.

Where the local authority is the purchaser of care, it has a responsibility to ensure that it knows who an individual's agent, appointee, attorney or receiver is and that he or she is party to the contract.

When a local authority is a provider of care through one of its homes it has the same responsibility and accountability as other home owners.

8.3 The home proprietor's accountability

The home proprietor is accountable to individuals or their representatives and the home's purchasing authority.

8.4 The home proprietor's responsibilities

8.4.1 Income

Where home proprietors are involved in managing individuals' money, they should ensure that all their income can be spent or saved by those individuals according to their instructions. The home must have a clear policy which sets out how this will be made possible.

They must ensure that systems are in place for recording any cash or valuables that are deposited with them.

8.4.2 Agent, appointee, attorney or receiver

A home proprietor may allow a member of staff to be the **agent** for the collection of an individual's State benefits. Where this happens, the home proprietor must ensure that all the money is handed over to that individual immediately it has been collected.

Where someone has no relative or friend who can be an **appointee** the home proprietor may suggest a suitable independent person to act in this capacity. It is only under exceptional circumstances that home proprietors or managers or their relatives should undertake the role of appointee.

Where home managers or care workers have been made agents or appointees, they should check that the Department of Social Security has informed the Registration and Inspection Unit in accordance with Local Authority Circular LAC(88)15 (1988).

No one connected with the home or their relatives should ever act as attorney or receiver.

See section 7.2 and Appendices C and D.

8.4.3 Confidentiality

The home proprietor must ensure that the systems in operation enable individuals or their representatives to receive information in a confidential manner.

Any financial information held by the home should be kept separately and securely from other information relating to the individual and be available only to that individual or people who have the authority to receive it.

The rules of confidentiality apply equally to all aspects of an individual's finances.

Where financial information is held on computer or database, the home must adhere to the regulations of the Data Protection Act 1984 and its various amendments.

8.4.4 Information

The home proprietor should ensure that information on how to obtain independent financial advice is available and that people know where that information is.

See section 9.4.

8.4.5 Enabling expenditure

Management should be aware of the importance of making it possible for individuals to spend their money.

8.4.6 Leaving a home

Details of any additional charges made when someone is leaving should be clearly stated in the home's brochure.

A home proprietor must ensure that individuals are given accurate and up-to-date information about any of their financial affairs in which the home has been involved when they leave.

All money held by the home for individuals must be paid to them in cash or as a cheque when they leave.

The home proprietor must ensure that appropriately signed receipts are obtained for such money.

8.4.7 Death

The home proprietor should encourage all individuals to state in writing, where possible, the arrangements they would like to make for their own funeral. The home should record the name of the relative or executor of the estate who is to make these arrangements.

The home proprietor should have a clear policy on how long after death the home will continue to charge for an individual's room.

All property, cash and valuables should be handed over only to the executor of the Will or, if the individual dies intestate, to the administrator of the estate. No one else has any legal right to a deceased person's property.

Any outstanding debts to the home are a charge against the person's estate.

Any loans made to the home by the individual are repayable immediately into the individual's estate.

See Appendix D.

8.4.8 Wills

The home proprietor should encourage all residents to make a Will. At the same time he/she should encourage them to prepare an enduring power of attorney.

Where the individual lacks the legal capacity to make a Will, the Court of Protection has the power to make a 'statutory Will' on the individual's behalf.

The home proprietor should have a clear policy about the acceptance of legacies by the home and its employees. Where the policy is that staff must decline all legacies, it is important that the individual is made aware of this.

If an individual wishes to leave money to a member of staff, it is inappropriate to suggest that the bequest is made to the home itself.

See Appendix D.

8.4.9 Complaints

It is a legal requirement that all registered homes should have a clear policy on how to act when there is a complaint. It is the home proprietor's responsibility to ensure that this policy is followed at all times.

All complaints must be recorded in a book and the proprietor must prove that they have been investigated and appropriate action taken.

The regulator must be informed of any serious complaint.

See Appendix C.

8.4.10 Theft

Where money and other valuables have been stolen, the home proprietor has a duty to ensure that the individual can report the theft to the police. Where the individual is unable to do so, the home proprietor should do so on the individual's behalf. This is irrespective of the sum involved and of whether the suspected thief is someone living in the home, an employee, relative or other visitor.

The conditions of service for staff should make it clear that any suspected financial abuse by staff in relation to an individual will be reported to the police. It should be made clear to staff that this is irrespective of the sum of money involved.

See Appendix B.

8.4.11 Protecting employees

Where a home proprietor manages an individual's money, the system operated by the home must include sensible controls to protect individuals, staff and managers and the home proprietor.

The system must protect both the individual whose money the home is managing from opportunities for fraud or theft and others who have access to it from the possibility of being accused of fraud or theft.

The system must be simple, respond quickly to demand and be easy to use and easy to maintain. It must also have clear-cut authorisation systems which are used and regularly checked. Good practice should ensure that such a system is regularly audited.

The home manager or a specified senior member of staff should be made responsible for the efficient and effective management and administration of individuals' money within the home.

Training appropriate to each member of staff's level of responsibility for an individual's money must be given before staff are required to take such responsibility. This training should be regularly updated.

The home proprietor should take appropriate steps to minimise the risk of assault to, or robbery from, employees who handle cash. This is particularly important where staff, acting as agents, collect benefits for several residents at once and where the home has substantial sums of money on the premises.

Steps could include obtaining advice from the local crime prevention unit and negotiating with the Benefits Agency to have benefits paid direct into individuals' bank accounts if they so wish.

8.5 Care workers' responsibilities

Care workers must make it possible for individuals to spend their money on whatever they wish, taking into account the limitations on choice discussed in section 6.2.

Care workers cannot refuse this responsibility as long as they have received adequate training or instruction and the home has appropriate standing procedures on the subject.

Care workers must not solicit gratuities.

9 | Enabling expenditure

Help individuals
if they wish

Everyone should be offered help to obtain their entitlements, and to manage, save and spend their money as they wish. This help should not be imposed on anyone.

9.1 Assisting those who cannot manage

Relatives, friends, advocates and care workers may need to provide considerable help, support and motivation to help people to spend their own money.

Anyone involved should be sensitive to the fact that individuals of different ages and disabilities have a wide variety of different needs. It should not be assumed that individuals and others involved have the same values.

See Appendix D.

9.2 Establishing priorities

It is often difficult to help people to plan the way in which their money should be spent.

Where appropriate, an advocate or relative should be involved in planning expenditure.

9.3 Helping people to budget

Teaching people to budget or enabling them to regain that skill can be a long process and they may need help for a considerable length of time.

People living in residential or nursing homes may have no idea what to spend their money on. Approaches which have been successful in various parts of the country in stimulating ideas have ranged from the use of magazines, mail order catalogues and holiday brochures to an exhibition mounted for individuals, their relatives and other interested parties on benefits, banking systems and ways of spending money.

Care workers and others must be prepared for individuals who are learning to budget and choose what to spend money on to make what others would consider inappropriate purchases.

9.4 **Financial advice**

Finding a good financial adviser is not easy. While personal recommendation is often the best solution, financial advice should always be from sources independent of the home proprietor.

People should be able to receive independent advice on all aspects of managing their finances. Where appropriate, this should include advice both from an advocate (see 6.1) and from a financial adviser who is a member of one of the financial regulatory bodies. A list of these can be obtained from the Personal Investment Authority on 0171-538 8860.

Advice should always be sought from more than one adviser. In addition to personally recommended advisers, those regularly quoted by the financial writers in newspapers' financial pages are worth considering.

See section 8.4.4.

10 | Protection

Keep it safe

Money and valuables kept in the home should be held securely. Appropriate controls should be in place to make this possible.

A home proprietor should operate a range of systems to cater for the different ways in which people want to keep their money and valuables, and for the various ways in which they want to have access to it.

See Appendix D.

10.1 Where money should be kept

Within a home people should have easy access to their own money and know where it is kept.

Individuals should have access to a secure, lockable facility in their own rooms in which they can keep small amounts of cash and valuables. There should be a communal safe for larger amounts.

Each individual should have his or her own identifiable bank or savings account.

If a composite account for a group of individuals exists, the interest earned must be allocated accurately to each person.

The accounts must not be part of any other accounts kept by the home proprietor.

Each account should be interest-bearing.

If, however, an account is not interest-bearing, the average balance should never be more than an individual's monthly income and the excess should be transferred to an interest-bearing account.

Each account should reflect good banking practice.

Individuals may choose to hold their money either in a bank or building society account maintained or especially opened for them or in an account managed by the home proprietor.

See Appendix D.

10.2 Cash; cheque or benefit order books; credit, debit or benefit payment cards

People should be able to keep cash, cheque or benefit order books, or credit, debit or benefit payment cards securely within their rooms.

For security reasons, it is sensible to encourage people to make sure that the cash sum is a modest one. However, facilities provided by the home should make it possible for at least one week's income to be kept as cash.

If individuals are likely to forget that they've got books or cards or money or how much, it is important that there is a system in place which will protect the staff from false accusations of theft.

10.3 Information

Account holders or their nominees should be informed of all transactions that have taken place in their account/accounts at least once every month. This information, which is strictly confidential, must be accurate, comprehensive and current.

See section 8.4.3.

10.4 Valuables

People should be able to bring valuable items with them into a home if they wish. However, they must be aware of the risk which they incur by doing so.

If the valuable items are small and easily removed, for example watches or jewellery, it is essential that the individuals and their visitors inform the home manager if these items are being removed. This is to prevent unnecessary searches and unfair accusations of theft.

Section 8.4.10 and Appendix D.

10.5 **Insurance**

Individuals should be aware of the level of cover provided by the home for their own cash and other valuables. Should they wish to keep money or valuables to a greater value than that covered by the home, they should be informed of the risk and encouraged to take out appropriate additional insurance.

See Appendix D.

10.6 **Staff's responsibilities**

Don't put staff at needless risk or temptation

All systems and procedures should ensure that staff involved in dealing with an individual's finances should be protected from unreasonable risk of loss, theft and unfair accusations. Clear, accurate, current and easily maintained records should be kept.

Failure by a home proprietor to keep such records may cause unnecessary accusations to be made against staff.

Care workers are responsible for enabling people to use their own money and should be careful to ensure that an individual's wishes are carried out after discussion with those who are assisting in financial management.

They must maintain the records and receipts from moneys spent on behalf of individuals, as required by the management system.

They must be aware of and follow the home proprietor's policy on gifts and be cautious that presents from individuals are not bribes or rewards.

Home managers must ensure that all staff receive appropriate training.

Care workers are responsible for ensuring that they do not get involved in the administrative aspects of individuals' finances for which they have not been trained.

Care workers who are responsible for collecting individuals' benefits in the form of cash on a regular basis must ensure that they follow the home's security policy to minimise the risk of their being robbed.

See section 8.4.11.

10.6.1 Confidentiality

Keep it confidential

Where money is handled by management or staff on behalf of an individual, both must ensure that confidentiality and privacy are maintained.

Benefits collected by a home on behalf of an individual must be handed over in the privacy of an individual's room.

Knowledge of an individual's savings, income and expenditure is confidential. Where care workers are involved, the information should be restricted to the minimum number of people who have a 'need to know'.

See section 8.4.3.

11 | Leaving a home

Make sure that full information is available

Individuals should be given accurate and up-to-date information about their financial affairs well before they leave the home.

They should be fully involved in the process of bringing the home's records up to date and in clarifying issues such as benefits and savings.

The criteria used to assess individuals' capacity to manage their financial affairs after leaving the home should be the same as those used while they were living in the residential or nursing home.

Individuals should receive any money held for them by the home at the time they leave, either in cash or as a cheque made payable to them. This will include any contribution, allowing for appreciation or depreciation, to a joint purchase.

They should give appropriately signed receipts for the money to the home.

See sections 8.4.6 and 6.2.8.

12 | Death

Individuals should make sure that the home knows who will be responsible for making their funeral arrangements when they die.

They should ensure that they have made a Will and that the home knows the name of their executor.

Any contribution to a joint purchase, adjusted for the item's appreciation or depreciation, must be paid into the individual's estate.

Any loans made to the home by individuals should be repaid to their estate by a date agreed with the executors. This should be no later than the granting of probate or letters of administration.

See sections 8.4.7 and 6.2.8.

13 | Complaints

13.1 Residential or nursing homes

All homes must have a clear policy for dealing with complaints. It is the home proprietor's responsibility to ensure that this policy is followed at all times.

The home proprietor should ensure that individuals and their relatives know how to make a complaint and that they are satisfactorily resolved within a reasonable, specified length of time.

See section 8.4.9.

13.2 National Assistance Act financial assessment

If individuals dispute the amount that they have been assessed as able to pay towards a home's fees, they should apply for reassessment under the procedure set up by the local authority. If this is refused, then the formal complaints procedure should be instigated. This is the recourse available for all aspects of community care, including the financial assessment. Disputes will occur mainly if there has been a mistake in the calculation of income or capital or if the interpretation of the rules is incorrect. If it is thought that the local authority has not used its discretion or has too rigid a policy or has not taken into account the circumstances of the case properly to see if discretion should be applied, the complaints procedure should be used.

At present, the procedure may differ depending on which local authority is involved. However, each authority should ensure that its procedure is readily available.

The Association of Metropolitan Authorities, the Association of County Councils and the Association of Directors of Social Services have prepared guidance on a model contract which, it is expected, will be used for all out-of-authority contracts, ie those outside the authority's geographical area. Although mediation should therefore be available if there is a dispute about the financial assessment, provision for this has not yet been established everywhere. Disputes can also be taken to arbitration through the Chartered Institute of Arbitrators, although this can be a very expensive procedure.

Other complaints about aspects of the assessment can be made through the local authority's formal complaints procedures.

Further information can be obtained locally from: Citizens Advice Bureaux, welfare rights services and social services departments.

Appendix A
Glossary of terms used in this book

Care manager Usually a social services employee who has probably been responsible for an individual's needs assessment under the NHS and Community Care Act 1990.

Care worker Any member of the home's staff who assists individuals to manage their money.

Home manager The employee of the residential or nursing home who has responsibility for its day-to-day management.

Home proprietor The person or company who owns and runs one or more residential or nursing homes. It is probable that that person or a named company director is the 'person registered' under the Registered Homes Act 1984 and is responsible for maintaining the standards required under its provisions and related regulations.

Individual The person who lives in a residential or nursing home. Although this guide refers to actions being taken by the individual, it is assumed that these actions may sometimes have to be carried out by someone acting on the individual's behalf.

Next of kin Individuals may choose to nominate any friend or relative as their next of kin to be notified in an emergency. They may also choose not to nominate anyone as next of kin.

Contrary to commonly held belief, the phrase 'next of kin' has no legal significance. The Mental Health Act 1983 defines the phrase as 'nearest relative' for the specific purposes of that Act.

Nursing home A nursing home provides accommodation, board and nursing care under the provisions of Part II of the Registered Homes Act 1984. It is required to be in the charge of a registered medical practitioner or first level registered nurse.

A mental nursing home provides accommodation, board and nursing or other medical treatment for mentally disordered patients under provisions of the Registered Homes Act 1984.

Personal expenses allowance The minimum amount of money retained by someone living in a residential or nursing home, where all other income has been used to pay the home's fees. It will not be paid if individuals have deprived themselves of capital or income in the circumstances described in the National Assistance (Assessment of Resources) Regulations SI 1992/2927 amended by SI 1993/964.

The personal expenses allowance is sometimes referred to as an individual's 'pocket money'. This is a pejorative term and should never be used.

Purchaser The purchaser is the person or authority who buys a place in a residential or nursing home. A health authority or trust may be the purchaser to fulfil its obligation to provide continuing care for an individual. A local authority may purchase accommodation under the NHS and Community Care Act. Where individuals pay for themselves, they act as the purchaser.

Relative The family member who is most closely involved and has taken most responsibility for the financial concerns of the individual. This person may not be the nominated next of kin or the person who visits most frequently.

Registration and inspection officer *See* Regulator below.

Regulator The regulations governing both the person who runs either a nursing or a residential home and the home itself are set out in the Registered Homes Act 1984, the 1992

Amendment to the Act (relating to small homes) and statutory regulations stemming from the legislation.

Once the registering authority has agreed to register a home, its role is to monitor, through inspection, the home's compliance with the requirements of the Acts. This is undertaken by the public regulator who is normally called the registration and inspection officer. Those for nursing homes are usually employed by a health authority and those for residential homes by a local authority. Some local authorities have joint inspection units with the health authority.

Residential home A residential home provides accommodation, board and personal care under the provisions of Part I of the Registered Homes Act 1984.

In the case of local authority-run residential homes, these are not registered in the same way as private and voluntary sector homes but they are inspected and required to meet the same standards.

Homes with a Royal Charter do not need to be registered.

Appendix B
Nursing homes: Regulations

Health Circular HC(81)18/Local Authority Circular
LAC(81)4 *Health Service Management: Registration and inspection of private nursing homes and mental nursing homes (including hospitals)*
Relevant extracts from the Circular

Part III

Complaints

22 It may be necessary from time to time to visit a home to investigate complaints about the standard of care or facilities provided in a registered home. The responsibility of the authority with regard to such complaints is to ensure that there has been no breach of the registration requirements. If complaints relate to the possible mistreatment of patients or the misappropriation of patients' moneys it may be necessary for the authority to refer the matter to the police. If such a complaint involves the 'person in charge' of the home and is upheld, it may ultimately lead the authority to decide that the individual concerned is not a fit person to be in charge of a home and ultimately lead it to consider cancelling the registration.

***Registration and inspection of nursing homes –
A handbook for health authorities*** (1985) National
Association of Health Authorities (NAHA)

Part 1 Advice to Health Authorities – Registration and
Inspection

3.38 **Brochure**

The publication by the proprietors of a nursing home of
a brochure available to the intending patients can form
a useful background of information for inspectors. It will
indicate, for example, the range of care the nursing home
purports to offer; whether it is offering services for which
dual registration would be appropriate, and the
accommodation and facilities available.

16.3 **Complaints**

If the complaints relate to such matters as the possible
ill treatment of patients or misappropriation of patients'
moneys it may be necessary for the Registering Authority
to refer the matter to the police.

Part 2 Model Guidelines – Registration and Inspection

3.11 **Brochure**

It is suggested that the proprietors of the nursing homes
produce a brochure for patients indicating the range of care
the nursing home offers, whether it is offering services for
which dual registration would be appropriate and the
accommodation and facilities available.

***Registration and inspection of nursing homes –
A handbook for health authorities 1988 supplement***
(1988) NAHA
Quality of life for the elderly, long-stay patient

2 **Policy**

2.1 Every nursing home should publish an information
brochure, supplied to enquirers as to the services it offers;
the type and level of patient dependency for which it
routinely cares; a description of the accommodation; of
the staffing and its management arrangements; and its
registration certificate.

3 The patient relationship

3.1 Nursing homes should be so managed and conducted that patients retain their personal dignity and maximum independence compatible with the limitations of their physical and/or mental infirmity.

iii Have their personal privacy respected.

ix Manage their own financial and personal affairs.

x Are aware of and have access to community and social facilities.

xi Have access to a relative, friend or adviser who as an 'advocate' has a facility to pursue matters on their behalf.

5 The relationship between staff and patient

5.1 This section is designed to assist the assessment of the 'qualitative' aspects. It is not just concerned with the physical attributes of the premises but also with the visibility to inspecting officers of the patients' lifestyles and the continuing processes of ascertaining and meeting the wishes and needs of the patients.

5.2.ii *Social needs*

f Does the patient have control of his/her personal and financial affairs.

Appendix C
Residential homes: Regulations

Residential Care Homes Regulations 1984
Relevant sections of the regulations: SI 1984/1345
amended by SI 1988/1192

Regulation 6

1 The person registered shall compile the records specified in schedule 2 to these regulations - and shall keep them in the home at all times, available for inspection by any person authorised in that behalf by the registration authority.

2 The person registered shall keep in a safe place in the home the case record of each resident compiled in accordance with paragraphs 4 and 5 of said schedule.*

Schedule 2

Paragraph 16:
A record of the scale of charges from time to time applicable, including any extras for additional services not covered by that scale, *and the amounts paid by or in respect of that resident.*

Paragraph 17 (amended in 1988):
A record of all money or other valuables deposited by a resident for safe keeping, or received on the resident's behalf, specifying the date on which such money or valuables were deposited or received and the date on which any sum or other valuable was returned to a resident or used at the request of the resident on his behalf and the purpose for which it was used.

Regulations 9 (1) and (2) – conduct of homes

1 The person registered shall arrange for the home to be conducted so as to make proper provision for the welfare, care and, where appropriate, treatment and supervision of residents.

2 In reaching any decision relating to a resident the person registered shall give first consideration to the need to safeguard and promote the welfare of the resident and shall, so far as is practicable, ascertain the wishes and feelings of the resident and give due consideration to the resident's wishes as is reasonable, having regard to the resident's age and understanding.

* para 4 states 'a case record in respect of each resident shall include details of any special needs of that resident, any medical treatment required by him including details of any medicines administered to him, and any other information in relation to him as may be appropriate including details of any periodic review of his welfare, health, conduct and progress'. . . para 5 relates to the special educational needs of children within the meaning of section 1 of the Education Act 1981.

Appendix D *Home Life*

Home Life – A Code of Practice for residential care
(1984) endorsed by the Secretary of State and applicable
to all sectors. A revised edition is to be published in
1996
The following relevant points are taken from Chapter 7
'Summary of Recommendations – a checklist'.

In order to clarify the status of items in this checklist, the
word 'must' has been reserved for legal requirements. The
legal basis of these requirements lies outside the Code.

Admission procedures
1 All homes should produce a brochure setting out the aims
of the establishment and the facilities which it intends to
provide.

9 Residents' personal possessions should be treated with
respect and any valuable items noted. Unobtrusive
procedures for the recording of major additions and
deletions should be established.

General administration
20 Professional advice and guidance from the registration
authority should be sought when the resident's ability to
make decisions or exercise choice appears to be in doubt.

21 All complaints should be treated seriously and recorded.

22 Residents should be made aware that they have the right
to refer any unresolved complaint to the registration
authority.

Financial affairs

42 Adults who are likely to be permanent residents should be encouraged to make a will prior to admission to the home.

43 Proprietors or staff should not act as witnesses to any resident's will. In no circumstances should the proprietor or any member of staff become the executor of any resident's will.

44 If a resident's incompetence to make a will is confirmed by a medical practitioner, consideration should be given to contacting the Court of Protection.

45 It should be the publicly-known practice of a home to decline all personal gifts from residents, except for small token presents. If a resident insists, independent advice, if possible from the registration authority, should be sought.

46 The acceptance of gratuities by staff should not be permitted.

47 Residents should be made aware of their responsibility for the safe-keeping of money and valuables, and of any insurance provided by the home which covers this. They should be advised to take out any further insurance which may be needed.

48 The home should have a secure facility, with limited access by a responsible person, for the storage of residents' valuables. Receipts should be given to depositors.

49 The home should also keep a permanent register of deposits and withdrawals.

50 In the case of temporary or permanent incapacity of a resident to safeguard his possessions, the agent acting on his behalf should undertake the responsibility (see 51–54).

51 The resident may appoint a relative, friend or someone over 18 in the community to act as his agent in the handling of his finances.

52 In the absence of someone known to the resident, the registration authority should be asked to recommend someone to act as the agent. References for agents should be sought, and all names of individuals and organisations

acting as agents should be lodged with the registration authority. Only in exceptional circumstances should the proprietor or manager assume the role of agent.

53 A resident wishing to delegate more extensive powers to act on his behalf may execute a power of attorney. No-one connected with the home should be appointed an attorney.

54 When a qualified medical practitioner has assessed a resident as mentally unable to manage his financial affairs, and the value of assets warrants it, careful consideration should be given to placing the resident under the jurisdiction of the Court of Protection.

55 In the case of children, guidance and education in the handling of personal money is good practice.

56 Proprietors and staff should not become involved in the handling and management of residents' moneys. They should be able to draw the attention of the registration authority to any concern they have about particular problems of a resident's finances.

Appendix E
Equipment for disability and therapy services equipment

Relevant paragraphs from *How to Get Equipment for Disability* (1993) compiled by Michael Mandelstam

24.4.2. Dental appliances

24.4.2.1. *Regulations (England and Wales)* clearly state that the private home owner has a duty to 'make arrangements, where necessary, for residents to receive dental services' (SI 1984/1345 r.10(p)). This refers to access to health service general dental practitioners, and the duty stands unless the resident requests that private arrangements be made instead.

24.4.2.2. *Circular guidance (England, Wales, Northern Ireland)* states that residents should have at least annual mouth examinations, and, if a family dentist is not available, the community dental service can be consulted. However, it states that residents should not benefit from treatment 'under the "priority" dental scheme or the school dental service' (DHSS, Welsh Office, 1977 para 20, HSS5(OS)3/78 para 21).

Other recent Circular guidance on the community dental service refers to the screening of residential homes (23.4.4.). It does not mention treatment in residential homes in particular, but states that any special needs group, with lack of access to a dentist, might need to be treated by the CDS (23.4.4.).

24.4.3. **Home nursing equipment** Circular guidance (England, Wales, Northern Ireland) states that when residents require nursing care, they should normally be seen by a district nurse (*DHSS, Welsh Office, 1977 para 17; HSS5(OS)3/78 para 18*).

'Home life' states that 'the right of residents to have access to community nursing services does not in any way put at risk the registration of the home as a residential care home' (*CPA 1984, p.28*). SSI (*1990a, p.27*) good practice issues include arrangements for nursing care.

In practice, this means that residents should have access to home nursing equipment. Circular guidance states that DHAs have the same power to provide such equipment to residents, as to people in their own homes (*see e.g. HRC(74)16; D(87)45 (re: incontinence pads) HSG(92)50*). However, there is some evidence that residents may be low priority and may not always receive community nursing services to an adequate level (*see e.g. B17.1.4.1.2. in this book; SSI (WO) 1989, p.17*).

24.4.3.1. *Cover of residential homes by district nurses* is likely to vary. For example, if each resident retains his or her own GP, a number of district nurses might cover the home. If one GP, by arrangement, is responsible for all the residents, then one district nurse might similarly be responsible for the whole home (*Eley M. Community Outlook. March 1989, pp.26–8*).

DHA/HB/HSSBs are normally expected to take responsibility for home nursing needs (through community nurses) in homes within their area, irrespective of the original home of the resident (*e.g. SSD (19) guidelines 1989*).

24.4.4. **Personal daily living equipment**

24.4.4.1. *Individual, personal need* Although the home might provide some daily living equipment for general use (see below), individual residents sometimes require equipment to meet an individual need.

Circular guidance (England, 1986) states that if the equipment is for an individual, then aids and equipment for use by that individual (e.g. walking aids and dressing aids) can be supplied by the SSD. Such supply should be on the same basis as supply to an individual in their own home (LAC(86)6).

24.4.4.1.1. **Waiting lists** In practice, waiting lists, and decisions on priority (2.5.7.2.), can mean that people in residential homes are sometimes accorded low priority in relation to community OT assessment. This is because they are seen to already be in care, and therefore not at the same degree of risk as a person living alone in their own home, for example. An SSI (WO) (1989, p.18) review found that therapists' involvement in homes varied in source, extent and purpose. For example, 31 homes (57% of the sample) received occupational therapy services.

The memorandum of guidance states that 'whenever possible remedial therapy should be provided to residents to alleviate disability or delay or prevent deterioration. Suitable aids and equipment should continue to be made available' (DHSS, *Welsh Office 1977, para 29*).

24.4.4.2. **Extent of SSD/SWD/HAAS responsibility** The SSD/SWD/HSSB might take responsibility for residents placed outside its area (*SSD guidelines 1989*).

SSD/SWD/HSSB internal guidelines sometimes state clearly that equipment is provided for individual use in private or voluntary residential homes, but not for common use (*Various SSD guidelines 1989/1990*).

There might be a joint policy to not provide equipment for individuals in homes which are joint registered (residential and nursing) (*SSD (23) guidelines 1989*); and occasionally a policy not to provide equipment at all to private residential homes (*SSD guidelines 1989*).

24.4.5. Equipment for mobility

24.4.5.1. **DHA/HB/HSSB physiotherapists** sometimes visit homes either to treat individuals or to give advice to care staff. Walking aids might then be loaned for individual need.

The extent to which physiotherapists visit residential homes is likely to vary from area to area. Residents, of course, can also attend hospitals (as outpatients) or health centres to see physiotherapists (via GP referral). An SSI (1988, p.19) review found that therapists' involvement in homes varied in source, extent and purposes. For example, 42 homes (78 per cent of sample) received physiotherapy services. SSI (1990a, p.27) good practice issues include arrangements for health care, including physiotherapy.

People in residential homes have the same entitlement to NHS paramedical services as people in their own homes. (*Hansard* 1990; *HSG(92) 50*)

24.4.5.2. **Private physiotherapists** might attend private residential homes, to treat individuals or to give exercise classes for example. Such physiotherapy might be integral to the home's services, or be charged to residents.

Equipment would normally have to be bought privately; or is sometimes hired out by the private physiotherapy service.

24.4.6. **Chiropody equipment** Circular guidance has made it quite clear that the health service has the same power to provide chiropody services to people in residential homes as to people in their own homes. (*HSG(92)50*)

In practice, with the shortage of NHS chiropodists, private practitioners might be used and charges made to the residents.

An SSI (1988, pp.15–16) review found that most (93%) homes received some chiropody services from the health service, although the extent of service was not always (44%) thought to be satisfactory. It stated, echoing the 1977 memorandum (*DHSS, Welsh Office para 21; HSS5(OS)3/78 para 22*), that chiropody services should be provided to residential homes by the health service and that SSDs should not have to pay for chiropody services.

SSI (1990a, p.27) good practice issues include arrangements for the provision of chiropody.

24.4.7. **Equipment for people with visual disability** 'Home life' states that there should be efficient lighting without glare, as well as colour contrasts, tactile clues (*CPA 1984, p.37*).

24.4.7.1. *Detection by care staff* Circular guidance (England/Wales/Northern Ireland) recommends that care staff should identify deterioration of vision in residents; district nurses and health visitors can assist staff in this identification. The care staff should also ensure that spectacles are cleaned and worn properly, and make necessary arrangements if some adjustment is needed. Sight-testing should be provided for residents. (*DHSS, Welsh Office, 1977 para 19, 20; HSS5(OS)3/78 para 19, 20*).

Circular guidance (Scotland, 1982), to similar effect, states that attending staff should be alert to visual impairment. If the resident cannot visit an optician's premises, the resident's GP can request, if necessary, a visit by the hospital eye service. Failing this, a local optician might visit the home (15.3.2.1.3.) (*NHS 1982(GEN)7*). An SSI review (*1988, pp.10–11*) found that homes' services to visually impaired residents varied. There was room for improvement, for example, in staff training in the use of special aids being used by residents; lack of attention to design features, eyesight testing, use of specialist SSD staff, checking of vision of elderly mentally disordered residents.

24.4.7.2. In practice, residents (should) have access (like people in their own homes) to the health service for spectacles, contact lenses and low vision aids; and to SSD/SWD/HSSBs for environmental daily living equipment for visual impairment. The SSI (*1988, appendix F and SSI 1990a, p.32*) 'performance rating' list includes the items:

- staff of home ensured residents' spectacles are clean and worn;

- home arranged regular sight testing for all residents;

- home staff took special steps to identify whether elderly mentally disordered residents developed sight problems;

- home used specialist SSD staff to help in the care of visually handicapped residents;

- home arranged for the provision of special aids for visually handicapped residents;
- home had any special design features to assist visually handicapped residents.

SSI (*1990a, p.27*) good practice issues include arrangements made for ophthalmology services.

24.4.8. Equipment for people with hearing impairment

24.4.8.1. *Environmental equipment for people with hearing impairment*
'Home life' recommends that the home should provide equipment such as radio aids, door alarms and other electronic aids for people with hearing impairment, as well as services to ensure the fitting, use and repair of aids and equipment (*CPA 1984, p.37*).

Circular guidance (England/Wales/Northern Ireland) recommends that environmental equipment such as loop systems, television adapters, amplified telephones need to be understood by both residents and staff. Such equipment might be chosen by the home following, for example, assessment by OTs (*DHSS, Welsh Office, 1977 para 29, 30; HSS5(OS)3/78 para 28, 29*).

An SSI review (*1988, pp.11–12*) found that the extent of staff awareness of the needs of hearing impaired residents and of special facilities varied. Few homes received hearing therapy services, though most had access to audiology clinics. Only a few homes made use of specialist SSD staff.

24.4.8.2. *Detection by care staff* Circular guidance (England, Wales, Northern Ireland) recommends that care staff should identify deterioration of hearing in residents; district nurses and health visitors can assist staff in this identification. The care staff need to understand the use and limitation of hearing aids, identify the need for new batteries or repair and inform the resident's GP of problems (*DHSS, Welsh Office, 1977 para 19, 20; HSS5(OS)3/78 para 19, 20*).

Circular guidance (Scotland 1982) is to similar effect, urging attending staff to be watchful, and noting that the resident's GP can be contacted, and if necessary, a domiciliary visit (to the residential home) made by specialist hospital services (*NHS 1982(GEN)7*).

24.4.8.3. In practice, residents (should) have access (like people in their own homes) to the health service for hearing aids; and to SSD/SWD/HSSBs for environmental daily living equipment for hearing impairment.

The SSI (*1990a, p.32 and 1988 appendix F*) 'performance rating' list includes:

- home staff ensured residents' hearing aids were working and were used;
- home staff took special steps to identify whether elderly mentally disordered residents developed hearing problems;
- home used specialist staff to help in the care of hearing impaired residents;
- home staff were offered special training on the needs of hearing impaired residents;
- the home had a loop system;
- the home had an adapted television set;
- the home had an amplified telephone.

25.2. Basis for equipment provision in private nursing homes

25.2.1. **Definition of nursing home** Legislation includes in its definition of nursing home: 'any premises used, or intended to be used, for the reception of, and the provision of nursing for, persons suffering from any sickness, injury or infirmity' (*e.g. Registered Homes Act 1984 s.21; Nursing Homes Registration (Scotland) Act 1938 s.10*).

25.2.2. Basis for standards: registration and inspection

25.2.2.1. *Legislation* places duties on DHA/HB/HSSBs concerning the registration and inspection of private nursing homes (*see Registered Homes Act 1984 and Registered Homes (Amendment) Act 1991 and SI 1984/1578; Nursing Homes (Registration) Scotland Act 1938 and Registered Establishments (Scotland) Act 1987 and SI 1990/1310 (S.143); Nursing Homes and Nursing Agencies (Northern Ireland) Act 1971; SR & O 1974/313; SI 1985/1775 (NI.9)*).

Legislation (England, Wales, Scotland) makes direct reference to duties to provide various equipment (*SI 1984/1578 r.12; SL 1990/1310 (S.143), r.13*).

25.2.2.2. *Circular guidance* has been issued with reference (in whole or in part) to equipment provision in private nursing homes. This is referred to, as appropriate, throughout the chapter.

25.2.2.3. *Guidelines*

25.2.2.3.1. *England and Wales.* The National Association of Health Authorities (NAHA) for England and Wales produced a 'Handbook on the registration and inspection of nursing homes' (1985). For DHAs, this was recommended by Circular guidance (England, Wales, 1984) as aiding the development of 'clear procedures for handling applications for registration and for use in monitoring homes once registered'. Its status, though, is that of advice; the contents are in no way binding (*HC(84)21; WHC(84)23*).

25.2.2.3.2. *Scotland.* Although the NAHA (25.2.2.3.1.) Handbook was produced for England and Wales, it has probably been used informally in Scotland.

However, the Scottish Home and Health Department (SHHD) has recently published its own 'Model guidelines for the registration and inspection of nursing homes for the elderly' (*SHHD, 1989*).This gives advice both to health boards and home owners, includes advice on equipment provision, and is referred to, as appropriate, throughout.

25.2.2.3.3. *Northern Ireland.* Detailed central (DHSS (NI)) guidance on inspection and standards seems not to have been issued, but HSSBs produce their own guidelines which seem to be based, to some extent, on the NAHA Handbook (25.2.2.3.1.).

25.4.3. Nursing equipment in private nursing homes

25.4.3.1 *Nursing home duty to provide nursing services and equipment.* Regulations state that the home owner has a duty to 'provide and maintain adequate' (England/Wales) or 'provide to an adequate standard or level' (Scotland) nursing equipment and treatment facilities (*SI 1984/1578 r.12; SI 1990/1310 r.3*).

In theory, this should apply to both nursing equipment for common use, and any nursing equipment needed for individuals. Circular guidance (England, Scotland) makes it quite clear that DHA/HBs should not provide nursing equipment (in general) to meet individual needs in private nursing (*see e.g. HRC(74)16 (England); NHS 1989(GEN)39 (Scotland)*). This is because the charges of the home should include any necessary 'nursing services or equipment' (*e.g. HRC(74)16*).

For example, a DH letter (1989) to an MP states that the reason for DHA non-provision of incontinence pads to private nursing homes is because such homes 'are under an obligation to provide continuous nursing care or treatment and generally fix their fees at a level which includes the costs of any nursing aids that may be needed' (*DH Letter POH(5)2143/141 22 May 1989 to Ann Winterton, MP*).

25.4.3.1.1. **DoH guidance describing arrangements from April 1993** Where people have entered private nursing homes following joint DHA/SSD assessment, the SSD 'is responsible for purchasing services to meet the general nursing care needs of that person, including the cost of incontinence services (eg laundry) and those incontinence and nursing supplies which are not available on NHS prescription'.

Health authorities will be responsible 'for purchasing, within the resources available and in line with their priorities the provision of specialist nursing advice, eg continence advice and stoma care' (*HSG (92) 50*).

This guidance does not extend to privately funded residents.

25.4.3.1.2. **Scotland** The position in Scotland is different in respect of incontinence pads. GPs in Scotland (unlike the rest of the UK) can prescribe bed incontinence pads.

Circular guidance has therefore advised that because private nursing home residents have access to their GPs who act as a 'trigger' for NHS services – GPs can prescribe bed incontinence pads to residents (*NHS 1989(GEN)39*).

Guidance has also stated, quite clearly, that health boards are obliged 'to supply incontinence aids to NHS patients in private nursing homes' on GP recommendation. This applies to aids not on the Drug Tariff, and to all residents (however funded) seeing their GPs on the NHS (*SHHD/DGM (1991) (67)*). The Scottish Office and DoH appear to be at variance on this issue.

25.4.3.2. **Practice** Some private nursing homes may charge the resident or his/her family extra for special items of nursing equipment, such as a special bed or special incontinence pads, not regarded as standard by the home (*Personal communications: several private nursing homes, 1990*).

Nevertheless, a well equipped nursing home provides as part of its normal equipment stock, for example: hoists (bath and mobile), walking frames, rollators, sanichairs, respirators ('suckers'), chairlifts, easy chairs (with high seat), headsets and amplifiers, adjustable height beds, monkey poles, adapted cutlery and incontinence pads. (*Personal communications: Registered Nursing Home Association, 1990*).

25.4.3.2.1. **Financial considerations** However, it is thought that not all private nursing homes are equipped as well as they might be.

Some home owners claim that one reason for this is that the level of DSS payments has not kept pace with inflation, thereby genuinely preventing home owners from providing the desired standards of service.

Another view is that, in some cases, levels of service provided by the home simply do not justify the level of charges made to residents.

25.4.4. **Paramedical services and equipment** The provision of health service physiotherapy, occupational therapy, speech therapy and chiropody services and equipment to individuals in private nursing homes seems in the past to have given rise, as Circular guidance (Scotland) points out, to misunderstanding (*NHS 1989(GEN)39*).

25.4.4.1. *Duty of home owner to provide adequate professional staff* Legislation (England, Wales, Scotland) places a duty on the home owner to provide adequate 'professional' staff, which could be taken to refer to paramedical staff (*SI 1984/1478 r.12; SI 1990/1310 r.13*).

25.4.4.2. **Practice** varies, from the home which provides such services integrally; to the home which provides them specially, at extra cost to the resident; to health service provision of such services or not, depending on local policies.

25.4.6. **Equipment for continence** Regulations state the home owner has a duty to provide adequate nursing equipment (see above); nursing equipment is expected to include incontinence pads, but see 25.4.3.1.2. above for position in Scotland.

Guidelines recommend that incontinence pads should be provided by the nursing home (*NAHA, 1985 p.103; NHSSB, 1988, p.43*).

25.4.10. **Hoists** Guidelines recommend that hoists should be provided, as necessary, by the home owner, and that care must be taken that they are used correctly and safely (*NAHA, 1985 p.103; NHSSB, p.43*).

25.4.12. **Steps and stairs, ramps** Guidelines recommend that steps and stairs should have handrails and be safely constructed and carpeted. Ramps should be non-slip (*NAHA, 1985, p.102; NHSSB, 1988, p.42*).

References

CPA (1984). Centre for Policy on Ageing. Home life: a code of practice for residential care. London, CPA, 1984.

D(87)45. Department of Health and Social Security. Provision of incontinence pads. London, DHSS, 1987.

DH Letter POH(5)2143/141 22 May 1989 to Ann Winterton MP.

DHSS(NI) (1991). Department of Health and Social Services (Northern Ireland). People First. Care management: guidance on assessment and the provision of community care. Belfast, DHSS(NI), 1991.

DHSS, Welsh Office (1977). Department of Health and Social Security; Welsh Office. Residential homes for the elderly: arrangements for health care. A memorandum of guidance. London, DHSS, WO, 1977.

Eley M. Community Outlook. March 1989, pp.26–8.

Hansard (1990). Mr Dorrell reply to Robin Cook; 26th July 1990.

HC(84)21. Department of Health and Social Security. Registration and inspection of private nursing homes and mental nursing homes (including private hospitals). London, DHSS, 1984.

HRC(74)16. Department of Health and Social Security. Statutory provisions: charges under section 2(2) of the National Health Service Reorganisation Act 1973. London, DHSS, 1974.

HSG(92)50. NHS Management Executive. Local authority contracts for residential and nursing home care after April 1993: NHS related aspects. London, DoH, 1992.

HSS5(OS)3/78. Department of Health and Social Services (Northern Ireland). Residential homes for the elderly – arrangements for health care. Belfast, DHSS(NI), 1978.

LAC(86)6. Department of Health and Social Security. Registration of residential homes. London, DHSS, 1988.

NAHA (1985). National Association of Health Authorities. Registration and inspection of residential homes: a handbook for authorities. Birmingham, NAHA, 1985.

NHS 1982(GEN)7 – SWSG 1982/2. Scottish Home and Health Department; Social Work Services Group. Care of the eyesight and hearing of elderly disabled people. Edinburgh, SHHD, SWSG, 1982.

NHS 1989(GEN)39. Scottish Home and Health Department. Private nursing homes: entitlement of patients to NHS supplies and services. Edinburgh, SHHD, 1989.

NHSSB (1988). Northern Health and Social Services Board. Registration and inspection of nursing homes: a code of practice for proprietors. Ballymena, NHSSB, 1988.

Nursing Homes and Nursing Agencies Act (Northern Ireland) Act 1971. Belfast, HMSO, 1971.

Nursing Homes Registration (Scotland) Act 1938. London, HMSO, 1938.

Registered Establishments (Scotland) Act, 1987. London, HMSO, 1987.

Registered Homes Act 1984. London, HMSO, 1984.

Registered Homes (Amendment) Act 1991. London, HMSO, 1991.

SHHD (1989). Scottish Home and Health Department. Model guidelines for the registration and inspection of nursing homes for the elderly. Edinburgh, SHHD, 1989.

SHHD/DGM (1991) (67). Scottish Office. Private nursing homes: entitlement of patients to NHS supplies and services. Edinburgh, Scottish Office, 1991.

SI 1984/1345. Residential Care Homes Regulations 1984. London, HMSO, 1984.

SI 1984/1578. The Nursing and Mental Nursing Home Regulations 1984.

SI 1985/1775 (NI.19). Nursing Homes and Nursing Agencies (Northern Ireland) Order 1985. Belfast, HMSO, 1985.

SI 1990/1310 (S.143). Nursing Homes Registration (Scotland) Regulations 1990. London, HMSO, 1990.

SR & O 1974/313. Nursing Homes (Registration, Conduct and Records) (Northern Ireland) Regulations 1974. Belfast, HMSO, 1974.

SSD Guidelines 1989 & 1990. Department of Health.

SSI (1988). Social Services Inspectorate. Health in homes: a review of arrangements for health care in local authority homes for elderly people. London, DoH, 1988.

SSI (1990a). Social Services Inspectorate. Guidance on standards for residential homes for elderly people. London, DoH, 1990.

SSI (WO) 1989. Social Services Inspectorate (Welsh Office). Residential care for elderly people – ensuring quality of care in the independent sector of Gwynedd. Cardiff, Welsh Office, 1989.

WHC(84)23. Welsh Office. Registration and inspection of private nursing homes and mental nursing homes (including private hospitals). Cardiff, Welsh Office, 1984.

Appendix F Capacity

An extract from *The Elderly Client Handbook* by District Judge Gordon Ashton published by the Law Society, 1994

Introduction

You must be able to recognise and cope with the legal implications of incapacity (sometimes referred to as *incompetence*).

Terminology

Terms in this context with distinct meanings are often applied as labels and used in a wrong context. A correct use of the common terms is as follows:

- an individual may suffer from an *illness* or *disorder*;
- this may result in a disability which comprises:
  – the limitation imposed upon the individual by reason of his or her physical, mental or sensory *impairment*; and
  – the *handicap* which this imposes on the individual in his or her environment;
- if the disability is of a sufficient degree the individual may be treated as legally *incapacitated* (or *incompetent*);
- this may be due to *mental incapacity* or *physical inability* or both.

Presumptions

There is a presumption that an adult is capable until the contrary is proved, but:

- this may be rebutted by a specific finding of incapacity;

- if a person is proved incapable of entering into contracts generally, the law presumes such condition to continue until it is proved to have ceased, although a lucid interval may still be proved;
- if an act and the manner in which it was carried out are rational, there is strong presumption that the individual was mentally capable at the time.

Causes of mental incapacity
Mental incapacity may arise by reason of:
- learning disability (previously called mental handicap);
- mental illness (which includes senile dementia);
- brain damage (which may be due to an accident or an illness).

Assessment
It would be convenient if people could be categorised as legally capable or incapable according to a simple test based upon a general assessment, but this would be discriminatory. Most individuals have some level of capacity and this should be identified and respected, so:
- legal definitions of mental capacity differ for different purposes;
- the severity of the test may depend upon the implications of the particular decision;
- the means of assessment vary.

In practice, assessments tend to be influenced by the perceptions of those applying them, so the method of assessment, whether formal or informal, may be more significant than the legal test to be applied.

Approaches
There are three possible approaches to the question of incapacity:
- *Outcome* – determined by the content of the decision (if it is foolish the maker must be incompetent).
- *Status* – judged according to the status of the individual (eg age, diagnosis or place of residence).

- *Understanding* – the ability of the individual to understand the nature and effect of the particular decision is assessed.

The status test has historically applied to infants but in some areas (eg medical treatment) it is giving way to the test of understanding. The understanding test is generally appropriate when dealing with adults, but in certain circumstances the status test may still apply, eg if a receiver has been appointed by the Court of Protection the individual ceases to have capacity in regard to financial affairs except to the extent that limited capacity is permitted by the Court (though the individual may retain capacity over personal decisions). Conversely, detention under the Mental Health Act does not automatically deprive the patient of legal capacity.

The outcome of a decision may result in a test of understanding being applied, eg

- an elderly spinster seeks to sell her substantial house for £900;
- a widow decides to go and live with her 'husband'.

Appearances

While the law is concerned with what is going on in the mind, society tends to be concerned with the outward manifestations. Note that:

- you must recognise the difference between *ability* and *capacity* as it is not unusual for communication difficulties to disguise mental capacity;
- appearance (perhaps the consequence of physical disabilities) can create an impression of mental incapacity which is not justified;
- conversely, the absence of physical characteristics may disguise an underlying mental disability.

Communication

A reasoning mind may be locked inside a body that lacks the ability to communicate in a normal manner. Every effort should be made to overcome communication problems using physical aids where these may assist, and if a simple response to questions is all that is possible (eg a raised eyebrow) take care to frame questions so that you do not have control over the outcome. Consider whether the person has received, retained and understood sufficient information on the basis of which to make a reasoned decision.

Criteria

When making assessments different professions apply different criteria and this should be borne in mind when seeking opinions about capacity:

■ the *medical profession* is concerned with diagnosis and prognosis, and health authorities are increasingly being relieved of the responsibility to care for those with mental disabilities who will not respond to medical treatment;

■ *care workers* classify people according to their degree of independence which involves consideration of levels of competence in performing skills such as eating, dressing, communication and social skills;

■ the *lawyer* is concerned with legal *competence* which means that the individual is capable of making a reasoned and informed decision (the test of *capacity*) and is able to communicate that decision.

Legal tests

The problem remains of identifying the legal definition or test of mental incapacity to be applied in any particular circumstances. There are different tests for different purposes, eg making a will, getting married, entering into a contract, signing an enduring power of attorney, being involved in court proceedings.

Mental disorder

The Mental Health Act 1983 contains several definitions which are adopted by other statutes. In particular 'mental disorder' is defined as:

'mental illness, arrested or incomplete development of mind, psychopathic disorder and any other disorder or disability of mind' (section 1).

This is intentionally wide because it was intended to identify individuals who need protection rather than restriction. Note that it does not involve any assessment of degree of impairment and that a mental illness or disorder does not necessarily result in incapacity; it is a matter of degree. The definition is sometimes used inappropriately in situations where the extent of the mental incapacity (rather than the fact of mental disorder) is in issue. In reality, it is little more than a screening process which may, or may not, be appropriate, ie 'incapable, by reason of mental disorder, of . . .'

Determining capacity

Where doubt is raised as to mental capacity:

- it is necessary to identify and apply the appropriate definition or test;

- you should consider whether the individual is incapable, because of the presumption of capacity;

- the question is not 'Is he incapable?' but 'Is he incapable of this particular act?';

- the question is one of fact though the correct legal test must be applied;

- capacity must be judged for each individual in respect of each transaction at that particular moment, as an individual may have a lucid interval;

- in legal proceedings a judge makes his determination not as medical expert but as a lay person influenced by personal observation and on the basis of evidence not only from doctors but also those who know the individual.

Evidence

- Evidence of conduct at other times is admissible, and the general pattern of life of the individual may be of great weight, although it is the state of mind at the time of the act that is material.

- Legal capacity depends upon understanding rather than wisdom so the quality of the decision is irrelevant as long as the person understands what he is deciding.

- General reputation is not admissible in evidence, but the treatment by friends and family of a person alleged to be suffering from mental disorder may be admissible as between them respectively.

■ Medical evidence is admissible and usually important, and it is for the court to decide whether the opinion of a medical witness has been formed on sufficient grounds and on the basis of the correct legal test.

■ An order of the Court of Protection based upon a finding of lack of capacity to manage affairs by reason of mental disorder is admissible as *prima facie* evidence of this fact.

Decision-making

Procedures are needed for decision-making on behalf of those who are deemed to be legally incapacitated (ie incapable of making or communicating their own decisions). This is considered in the Law Commission consultation papers.*

Types of decision

There are various fields of decision-making:

Management
■ financial matters (eg claiming benefits, managing money);
■ legal matters (eg buying property, making a will, court proceedings);

Personal
■ day-to-day living (eg what to eat or wear, to have a bath or a haircut);
■ activities involving more risk (eg going out alone, holidays);
■ major decisions (eg where to live);
■ highly personal decisions (eg getting married);

Medical
■ minor routine (eg dentistry, cervical smear tests, vaccinations);
■ treatment with advantages and disadvantages (eg optional minor surgery);
■ controversial treatment (eg sterilisation, participation in medical research);
■ refusal of medical treatment (eg to prolong life).

Procedures

Not all decisions can be delegated, either because they are too personal or the law does not make any provision. The law only makes specific provision for:

- decisions of a management nature; and
- medical treatment for certain mental disorders.

Recently, by using the 'declaration' procedure, the courts have attempted to enable significant medical decisions to be taken on behalf of mentally incapable people where previously such decisions could not be made because there was no procedure. Other minor personal and medical decisions are taken by carers and doctors of necessity without any legal authority or are simply not taken at all. The absence of approved procedures causes problems and uncertainty throughout the whole range of personal decision-making.

Basis of decisions

There are two approaches to making a decision on behalf of an incapacitated person:

- *best interests* – that which the decision-maker considers is best for the individual;
- *substituted judgment* – that which the individual would have chosen if capable of making the decision.

Both present problems, the former because it denies individuality and poses the risk of the decision-maker imposing his or her view as to what is best, and the latter because in many cases it cannot be conjectured what the individual would have wished. The Law Commission has proposed that a decision-maker should act in the best interests of the incapacitated person, taking into account:

- his or her ascertainable past and present wishes and feelings;
- the need to encourage and permit him or her to participate in any decision-making to the fullest extent of which he or she is capable; and

- the general principle that the course least restrictive of his or her freedom of decision and action is likely to be in his or her best interests.

* *Mentally Incapacitated Adults and Decision-making: A new jurisdiction* (1993); *Mentally Incapacitated Adults and Decision-making: Medical treatment and research* (1993); and the final report *Mental Incapacity* (1995).

Appendix G
Who can act for individuals?

Who can spend money on behalf of an individual with and without capacity?

Individual with capacity

	Individual	Agent	Ordinary power of attorney
Collect State benefit	yes	yes	yes
Spend State benefit	yes	no	yes
Spend other money	yes	no	yes

Individual lacking capacity

	Appointee	Receiver	Enduring power of attorney
Collect State benefit	yes	yes	yes
Spend State benefit	yes	yes	yes
Spend other money	no	yes	yes

Who can act for those who cannot collect State benefits or who lack capacity?

	Agent	Appointee	Receiver	Enduring power of attorney
Relative	yes	yes	yes	yes
Friend	yes	yes	yes	yes
Financial adviser	yes	yes	yes	yes
Independent advocacy service	yes	yes	yes	no
Health authority	yes	yes	yes	no
Local authority	yes	yes	yes	no
Home proprietor	yes	last resort	last resort	no
Home employee	yes	no	no	no
Public Trustee	no	yes	yes	no

Some health authorities continue to act for patients whom they have discharged into the community. Some local authorities act for individuals for whom they have purchased care.

Appendix H Further reading

Association of Metropolitan Authorities, Association of County Councils, Association of Directors of Social Services (1994) *Guidance on contracting for residential and nursing home care for adults.*

Ashton G (1994) *The Elderly Client Handbook*, The Law Society.

Ashton G (1995) *Elderly People and the Law*, Butterworth.

Centre for Policy on Ageing (1982) *Home Life* (revised edition to be published 1996).

Disability Alliance *Disability Rights Handbook*; annual with quarterly updates.

Dunning A (1995) *Citizen Advocacy with Older People*, Centre for Policy on Ageing.

Letts P (1990) *Managing Other People's Money*, Age Concern England.

Mandelstam M (1993) *How to Get Equipment for Disability*, Kogan Page and the Disabled Living Foundation.

Appendix I Useful addresses

Age Concern England
Astral House
1268 London Road
London SW16 4ER
Tel: 0181-679 8000

Benefits Agency
PO Box 51, Heywood
Lancashire OL10 2GG
Tel: 015320 324000

Centre for Policy on Ageing
25–31 Ironmonger Row
London EC1V 3QP
Tel: 0171-253 1787

Court of Protection
Stewart House
24 Kingsway
London WC2 6JX
Tel: 0171-269 7300

MENCAP
117–123 Golden Lane
London EC1 0RT
Tel: 0171-454 0454

MIND (National Association
for Mental Health)
Granta House
15–19 Broadway
London E15 4BQ
Tel: 0181-519 2122

**National Association
of Inspection and
Registration Officers**
28 Broom Lane
Rotherham
Yorkshire SE60 3EL
Tel: 01709 6237

Public Trust Office
Stewart House
24 Kingsway
London WC2 6HD
Tel 0171-269 7358

Relatives Association
5 Tavistock Place
London WC1H 9SS
Tel: 0171-916 6955

**RCN Society for
Nurse Inspectors and
Registration Officers**
Royal College of Nursing
20 Cavendish Square
London W1M 0AB
Tel: 0171-409 3333

Appendix J
Organisations consulted

The following organisations assisted in the development of this guide.

- Action on Elder Abuse
- Age Concern Berkshire
- Age Concern England
- Age Concern Institute of Gerontology
- Alzheimer's Disease Society
- Association of Charity Officers
- Association of County Councils
- Association of Metropolitan Authorities
- Benefits Agency
- British Federation of Care Home Proprietors
- College of Occupational Therapists
- Counsel and Care
- Homelife DGAA
- Independent Healthcare Association
- Lancashire County Council
- The Law Society
- MENCAP
- Wales MIND
- National Association of Health Authorities and Trusts
- National Association of Inspection and Registration Officers
- National Care Homes Association
- Public Trust Office

- Registered Nursing Homes Association
- Relatives Association
- Rescare
- Royal College of Nursing, Society of Inspection and Registration Officers
- Social Services Inspectorate
- Scope (formerly the Spastics Society)
- Unison

About Age Concern

Residents' Money: A guide to good practice in care homes is one of a wide range of publications produced by Age Concern England, the National Council on Ageing. Age Concern England is actively engaged in training, information provision, fundraising and campaigning for retired people and those who work with them, and also in the provision of products and services such as insurance for older people.

A network of over 1,400 local Age Concern groups, with the support of around 250,000 volunteers, aims to improve the quality of life for older people and develop services appropriate to local needs and resources. These include advice and information, day care, visiting services, transport schemes, clubs, and specialist facilities for older people who are physically and mentally frail.

Age Concern England is a registered charity dependent on public support for the continuation and development of its work.

Age Concern England
1268 London Road
London SW16 4ER
Tel: 0181-679 8000

Age Concern Scotland
113 Rose Street
Edinburgh EH2 3DT
Tel: 0131-220 3345

Age Concern Cymru
4th Floor
1 Cathedral Road
Cardiff CF1 9SD
Tel: 01222 371566

Age Concern Northern Ireland
3 Lower Crescent
Belfast BT7 1NR
Tel: 01232 245729

Publications from ▲C⬥E Books

A wide range of titles is published by Age Concern England under the ACE Books imprint.

Health and care: Professional handbooks

Health Care in Residential Homes
Dr Anne Roberts
Written in response to widespread demand for a book on this subject, *Health Care in Residential Homes* provides clear and straightforward information for managers and other care staff on maintaining residents' health and dealing with their health problems. Topics covered include the common illnesses of later life, the medicines prescribed, health promotion, what to do in an emergency and coping with terminal illness and bereavement.
£14.95   0–86242–156–X

Health and Safety in Care Homes: A practical guide
Sarah Tullett
This book is a complete reference manual to health and safety in care homes. It contains full coverage of issues such as UK and European Union legislation, risk assessment, equipment and hazardous substances – all the while encouraging managers and proprietors to assess their own health and safety provision and adapt the information provided to their own situations.
£9.95   0–86242–186–1

Expanding Care: A practical guide to diversification for care homes
Jenyth Worsley
This handbook outlines some of the ways in which care homes can diversify their activities – including the provision of domiciliary, day and respite care. It offers advice on assessing local needs, marketing and tendering, and explores the practical arrangements surrounding implementation.

£14.95   0–86242–154–3

Taking Good Care: A handbook for care assistants
Jenyth Worsley
Written for professional carers of older people, this book covers such vital issues as the role of the care assistant in a residential home, communication skills, the medical and social problems encountered by carers, the resident's viewpoint, and activities and group work.

£6.95   0–86242–072–5

Good Care Management: A guide to setting up and managing a residential home
Jenyth Worsley
This companion volume to *Taking Good Care* has been written for care home proprietors and managers, present and prospective. Topics covered include setting up a home, contracts, budgetary planning, staff management and training, the management of care and quality control.

£9.95   0–86242–104–7

Dementia Care: A handbook for use in residential and day care
Alan Chapman, Alan Jacques and Mary Marshall
The number of dementia sufferers requiring care is increasing continuously. This practical guide for professional carers offers an understanding of the condition and provides advice on such issues as daily care, health maintenance, home design and staffing strategies.

£9.95   0–86242–128–4

Reminiscence and Recall: A guide to good practice
Faith Gibson
Reminiscence work is acknowledged as a successful therapy in the care of older people. This new guide provides practical advice on planning and running reminiscence activity in a residential or day care setting and examines suitable approaches for people with particular conditions.

£9.95   0–86242–142–X

Arranging Outings for Older People: A group organiser's guide
Nancy Tuft
The definitive guide to the arrangements which need to be made when organising outings for groups of older people. Topics addressed include canvassing views, preparation and planning, making bookings and contingency arrangements. Lots of useful checklists are included.

£4.95   0–86242–141–1

Money matters

Your Rights: A guide to money benefits for older people
Sally West
A highly acclaimed annual guide to the State benefits available to older people. Contains current information on Income Support, Housing Benefit and retirement pensions, among other matters, and provides advice on how to claim them.

For further information please telephone 0181-679 8000.

Your Taxes and Savings: A guide for older people
Peta Hodge and Sally West
This definitive annual guide to financial planning provides a comprehensive explanation of the impact of taxation on the finances of older people. It also looks at managing retirement income and evaluates the wide range of investment opportunities available. Advice is given on building an investment portfolio and seven model portfolios are included.

For further information please telephone 0181-679 8000.

Managing Other People's Money
Penny Letts
Foreword by the Master of the Court of Protection
The management of money and property is usually a personal and private matter. However, there may come a time when someone else has to take over on either a temporary or a permanent basis. This book looks in detail at those circumstances and provides a step-by-step guide to the arrangements which have to be made.
£5.95   0–86242–090–3

If you would like to order any of these titles, please write to the address below enclosing a cheque or money order for the appropriate amount made payable to Age Concern England. Credit card orders may be made on 0181-679 8000.

Mail Order Unit
Age Concern England
PO Box 9
London SW16 4EX

Information factsheets

Age Concern England produces over 30 factsheets on a variety of subjects. Among these the following titles may be of interest to readers of this book:

Factsheet 7 *Making your Will*

Factsheet 18 *A brief guide to money benefits*

Factsheet 22 *Legal arrangements for managing financial affairs*

To order factsheets

Single copies are available free on receipt of a 9″ × 6″ sae. If you require a selection of factsheets or multiple copies totalling more than five, charges will be given on request.

A complete set of factsheets is available in a ring binder at a cost of £36, which includes the first year's subscription. The current cost for annual subscription for subsequent years is £17. There are different rates of subscription for people living outside the UK.

For further information, or to order factsheets, write to:
Information and Policy Department
Age Concern England
1268 London Road
London SW16 4ER

Index

registration and inspection of 81
  and severe disability premium 19
Public Trustee 45
purchasers: definition 65

radio aids 80
ramps 85
receivers 21, 43, 97, 98
  changing 47
  choosing 44–46
  problems involved 46–47
  staff members as 49
receivership orders 43–44
records, keeping 58, 70, 71, 72
Registered Homes Act 1984 12, 24, 64, 65
registration and inspection
  of nursing homes 17, 65–66, 81–82
  of residential homes 17, 66
Registration and Inspection Unit 17, 49, 66
regulators 17, 65–66
Relatives Association 47
relatives
  as appointees 44–45
  giving help with spending 54–55
  rights and responsibilities 16
  see also next of kin
residential homes 66
  aids and equipment 36–37, 38, 76–77
  brochures 72
  complaints procedures 17, 52, 72
  leaving 50, 60
  legal rights 24
  medical and therapy services 36, 37–38, 75, 76–78
  record-keeping in 70, 71
  registration and inspection of 17, 66, 76
  treatment of residents 71
    with hearing impairment 80–81
    with visual disability 79–80
  see also financial affairs; home proprietors
Royal Charter, homes with 66

safes, communal 56
savings 30–31
  and Income Support 31
savings accounts 56–57
Scotland 82, 83–84
SDP see severe disability premium
security 13, 56, 57, 73
severe disability premium (SDP) 19
short orders 44
spectacles 38
  care of 79
speech therapy 37
  in private nursing homes 84–85
stairs and steps 85
sub-letting of rooms 25, 33

teeth, care of see dental services
telephones, amplified 80
television adapters 80
temporary admission: and allowances 18
theft
  by staff 52
  protecting staff from accusations of 52–53, 57, 58
therapy services 37–38, 77–78
  in private homes 78, 84–85
tips see gifts and gratuities

understanding
  assistance with 15
  tests for 91

valuables 56, 57–58, 73
  insuring 15–16, 58, 73
  keeping records of 49, 70, 72, 73
visitors' expenses 35
visual disability, people with 38, 79–80

waiting lists 77
walking aids 37, 38, 77
Wills 51, 61, 73